LAUNCH INTO LITERATURE II

Primary Literature Program

for Grades 1-4 which

Encompasses Thirty-Six Noted

Children's Books

by
E.V. Stafford

Cover Illustration By
Jane Shasky

Inside Illustrations By
Liza Sernett

Publishers
T.S. Denison & Company, Inc.
Minneapolis, MN 55431

T.S. Denison & Company, Inc.
No part of this publication may be reproduced or transmitted by any means, mechanical or electronic, including photocopy, recording or stored in any information storage or retrieval system without permission from the publisher. Reproducible pages may be duplicated by the classroom teacher for use in the classroom, but not for commercial sale. Reproduction for an entire school or school system is strictly prohibited.

Standard Book Number: 513-02058-6
Launch Into Literature II
Copyright © 1990 by the T.S. Denison & Co., Inc.
Minneapolis, MN 55431

Table of Contents

Launch Into Literature II

Book List

Books	Grades	1	2	3	4	Tchrs Guide Page	Stdnt Repro Page

Single Sitting Picture Books

Books	1	2	3	4	Tchrs Guide Page	Stdnt Repro Page
1. *Rosie's Walk* – Hutchins	X				1	3
2. *The Very Hungry Caterpillar* –Carle	X				1	3
3. *Madeline* – Bemelmans	X	X			1	3
4. *The Story of Ping* – Flack and Wiese	X	X			1	3
5. *Leo the Late Bloomer* – Kraus	X	X			1	3
6. *Corduroy* – Freeman	X	X			1	3
7. *The Napping House* – Wood	X	X			1	3
8. *Make Way for Ducklings* – McCloskey	X	X			1	3
9. *Katie No Pockets* – Payne	X	X			1	3
10. *Harry the Dirty Dog* – Zion	X	X			1	3
11. *Little Toot* – Gramatky	X	X			1	3
12. *Bread and Jam for Francis* – Hoban	X	X			1	3
13. *Katy and the Big Snow* – Burton	X	X			1	3
14. *Spectacles* – Raskin	X	X	X		1	3
15. *Imogene's Antlers* – Small	X	X	X		1	3
16. *A Chair for My Mother* – Williams	X	X	X		1	3
17. *Mike Mulligan and His Steam Shovel* – Burton	X	X	X		1	3
18. *If I Ran the Zoo* – Seuss	X	X	X		1	3
19. *Alexander and the Wind-Up Mouse* – Lionni	X	X	X	X	1	3
20. *The Tenth Good Thing About Barney* – Viorst	X	X	X	X	1	3
21. *Amelia Bedelia* – Parish	X	X	X	X	1	3
22. *Cloudy With a Chance of Meatballs* – Barrett	X	X	X	X	1	3
23. *The Wednesday Surprise* – Bunting	X	X	X	X	1	3
24. *Why Mosquitoes Buzz in People's Ears* – Aardema	X	X	X	X	1	3

Chapter Books

Books	1	2	3	4	Tchrs Guide Page	Stdnt Repro Page
25. *Frog and Toad All Year* – Lobel	X	X			1	5
26. *A Lion to Guard Us* – Bulla	X	X	X	X	1	5
27. *The Drinking Gourd* – Monjo	X	X	X	X	1	5
28. *Help! I'm a Prisiooner in the Library* – Clifford	X	X	X	X	1	5
29. *Freckle Juice* – Blume	X	X	X	X	1	5
30. *Fantastic Mr. Fox* – Dahl	X	X	X	X	1	5
31. *The Mouse and the Motorcycle* – Cleary		X	X	X	1	5
32. *Mr. Popper's Penguins* – Atwater		X	X	X	1	5
33. *Paddle-to-the-Sea* – Holling			X	X	1	5
34. *The Enormous Egg* – Butterworth			X	X	1	5

Poetry

Books	1	2	3	4	Tchrs Guide Page	Stdnt Repro Page
35. *A Light in the Attic* – Silverstein	X	X	X	X	1	11
36. *Hailstones and Halibut Bones* – O'Neill		X	X	X	1	9

OVERVIEW

The purpose of Launch Into Literature is to introduce 1st-4th grade students to good literature and improve their reading abilities in the process. This is accomplished by using a powerful reading lesson design and student activities that stimulate higher order thinking skills. Revolving around thirty-six books written by prominent authors, all of the stories have won awards or are generally recognized as classics in their field. The titles will be familiar to most primary teachers and represent a variety of cultural, ethnic and human experiences.

The three types of books presented in this project are:

Single Sitting – those that can be read in on sitting.

Chapter – those read over a period of time, and

Poetry – which can be used as periodic single-sitting literature or chapter books and read straight through.

The format is designed for the teacher to discuss an aspect of the story with the students, read aloud to them and follow it with a variety of critical thinking questions and high-interest activities.

Each Book treatment consists of:

TEACHER'S GUIDE PAGE – (Non-reproducible)

- **Before/After Reading Activities** – These simple activities connect students experiences to the reading and take them into, through and beyond the story in a way that piques their interests. This powerful technique is stressed in the book, *Becoming A Nation of Readers* and has been proven to dramatically increase comprehension.

- **Critical Thinking Questions** – These questions have no right or wrong answers and stimulate thinking about character motivation, problem solving, predicting outcomes, etc. Emphasis is placed on the upper level of Bloom's Taxonomy: Analysis, Synthesis and Evaluation.

- **Thematic/Whole Language Activities** – Provides activities related to the reading in other areas of the curriculum: math, science, language arts, social studies, art, etc. They all involve reading, writing, listening and speaking; thus constituting a whole language approach to literature.

- **Extended Reading List** – Present other books by the same author and related books, also. This gives direction to students when choosing books to read on their own. It is also useful for teachers wishing to pursue an author or subject matter.

STUDENT PAGES (Reproducible)

- Designed to stimulate critical and creative thinking, few activities have right/wrong answers. Writing is also an integral part of the activities because it is necessary in a whole language approach to the literature.

- Each activity sheet has the subject area and the specific skill it reinforces indicated in the upper right-hand corner of the page. For chapter and poetry books the specific chapter or poem that correlates to the worksheet is written at the bottom of the page.

The important skills developed in the student activity pages are:

Prepositions	Personal Awareness	Cause/Effect
Analytic Thinking	Puppets	Creative Thinking
Comprehension	Critical Thinking	Values Clarification
Creative Expression	Adjectives	Measuring/Cooking
Categorization	Color Words	Narrative Writing
Number Words	Similarities/Differences	Compare/Contrast
Writing	Graphing	Expository Writing
Predicting Outcomes	Personal Expression	Creative Writing
Letter Writing	Poetry	Drawing Conclusions
Mapping	Songwriting	Character Development

Easy to use and readily implemented in any primary classroom, *Launch Into Literature II* embodies all the best in children's literature and reading lesson design.

ROSIE'S WALK
Pat Hutchins

BEFORE READING ACTIVITY

If you were a hen, where are some places you could walk on a farm? (Discuss.)

Rosie is a hen and she takes a walk on the farm. See where she goes and who is following her.

AFTER READING ACTIVITY

Where did Rosie go on the farm? (Draw and list on board.)
Where else do you think she could have gone?

CRITICAL THINKING QUESTIONS

- Do you think Rosie knew the fox was following her? Why, why not?
- Will the fox try to get her again? Why, why not?

THEMATIC/WHOLE LANGUAGE ACTIVITIES

Science	• Study animals.
Language Arts	• (Prepositions) Students fold paper into fourths and draw what teacher says:
Example:	"Box 1 – Draw a ball *under* a table."
	"Box 2 – Draw a hen *beside* a barn."

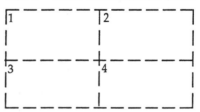

EXTENDED READING

Other books by Pat Hutchins:

Good Night Owl
The House that Sailed Away
The Surprise Party
The Curse of the Egyptian Mummy
King Henry's Palace
One Hunter

Name _____

Cut out and paste the picutres in the right place.

OVER   **UNDER**

Name _____

Draw other places Rosie could go on the farm.

In her house.

Under the fence.

fold #1

4.   3.   fold #2

1.   2.

by:

Rosie's Walk

Rosie went over the hay.

THE VERY HUNGRY CATERPILLAR
Eric Carle

BEFORE READING ACTIVITY

What kinds of things do you think a hungry caterpillar might eat? (Discuss.)

This is the story about a very hungry caterpillar, lets's see what it eats.

AFTER READING ACTIVITY

How are the foods the little caterpillar ate the same as you eat? How are they different? (Draw/write responses.)

Examples:	Same	Different	
	pie	leaf	(unless students
	orange		include lettuce)
	sausage		

CRITICAL THINKING QUESTIONS

- Do you think caterpillars really eat pie? Why, why not?
- What do you think a hungry caterpillar might eat? Why?

THEMATIC/WHOLE LANGUAGE ACTIVITIES

Art
- Students make their own cocoons out of construction paper or paper mache.
- Make caterpillar collage out of tissue paper like the illustrations in the book.

Science
- Study the life cycle of a butterfly.
- Compare and contrast the foods a caterpillar eats and a butterfly eats.

Language Arts
- Students write or dictate their own stories about what the hungry caterpillar ate.
- Tear a hole in paper, students draw around it what the caterpillar ate and dictate/write a story about it.

EXTENDED READING

Other Books by Eric Carle:
The Grouchy Ladybug
Do You Want to be My Friend?
The Mixed-up Chameleon
The Secret Birthday Message
The Very Busy Spider

LANGUAGE ARTS:
Creative Expression

Name ——————————————————————————

Color and cut out the caterpillar and the butterfly. Paste the handles on the back.
Put on a puppet show.

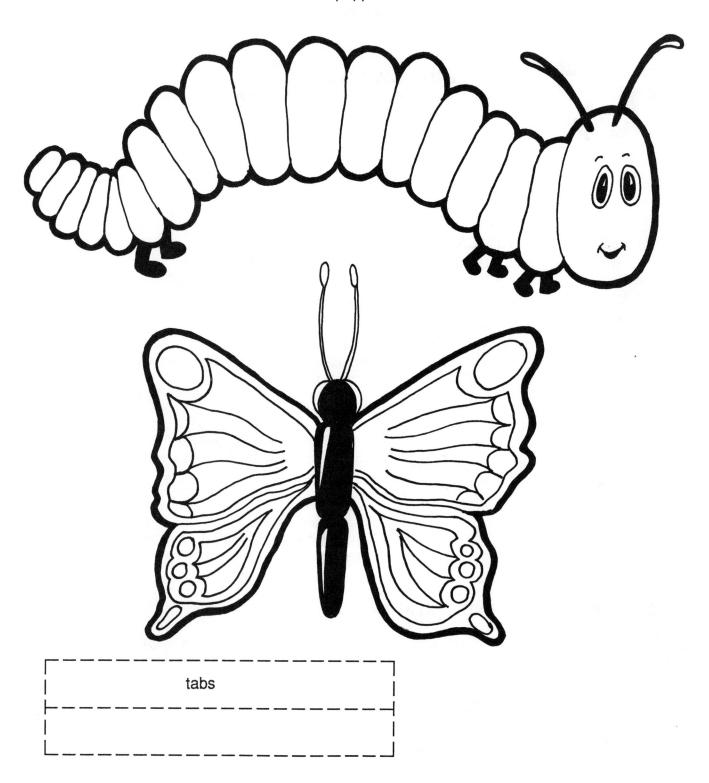

tabs

The Very Hungry Caterpillar

Name _____

Cut out each fold book. Cut the hole out of all the pages.
Draw what the caterpillar eats in one book. Then draw what you eat in the other book.

Book 1: The Very Hungry Caterpillar

3.

It ate a

---- fold ----

2.

It ate a

---- fold ----

1.

The Very Hungry Caterpillar

by: _____

Book 2: I Am Very Hungry

3.

I ate a

---- fold ----

2.

I ate a

---- fold ----

1.

I Am Very Hungry

by: _____

Name _____

Choose an animal. Draw and write your own story.

The Very Hungry _____.

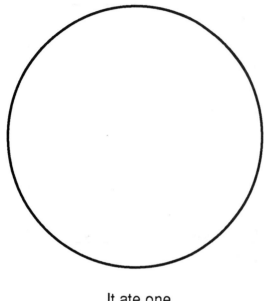

It ate one

_____

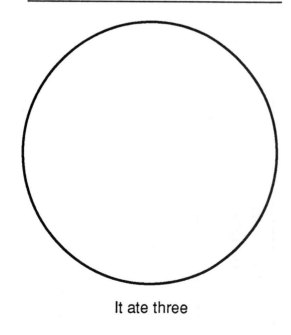

It ate three

_____

It ate two

_____

MADELINE
Ludwig Bemelmans

BEFORE READING ACTIVITY
Have you ever thought being sick would be better than being well? (Discuss.)

This is the story of Madeline who gets sick one day.

AFTER READING ACTIVITY
What are things you can do when you're sick? What are the things you can do when you're well? (List on board.)

Sick	*Well*
_____	_____
_____	_____
_____	_____

CRITICAL THINKING QUESTIONS
• Would you like a friend like Madeline? Why, why not?
• Why do you think all the girls wanted their appendix out?

THEMATIC/WHOLE LANGUAGE ACTIVITIES

Social Studies	• Learn about Paris.
Science/Health	• Discuss how to take care of yourself when you're sick and when you're well.
Language Arts	• Write stories about Madeline.

EXTENDED READING
Other books about Madeline:
Madeline and the Bad Hat
Madeline and the Gypsies
Madeline in London
Madeline's Rescue

Name _____

What present would you take to Madeline in the hospital? Why?

I would bring Madeline _____

because _____

_____.

Name _____

What do you think Madeline will do when she gets out of the hospital?

She will _____

_____

Next she will _____

_____

Then she will _____

_____

Name _____

Write a letter to Madeline in the hospital.

Dear Madeline,

_____

_____

_____

_____

_____

_____

_____

_____

_____

Your Friend,

_____

THE STORY ABOUT PING
Marjorie Flack and Kurt Wiese

BEFORE READING ACTIVITY

What would you do to avoid getting a spanking? (Discuss.)

This is the story about a duck named Ping who didn't want a spanking either. See what he does.

AFTER READING ACTIVITY

Chaining: What would have happened if Ping never found his home again?

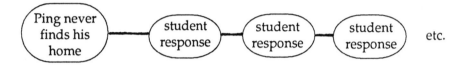

Ping never finds his home — student response — student response — student response — etc.

CRITICAL THINKING QUESTIONS

- Do you think Ping will ever stay away from home again? Why, why not?
- How do you think his family felt when he was away? Why?
- What do you think happened to the boy who set Ping free?

THEMATIC/WHOLE LANGUAGE ACTIVITIES

Social Studies • Learn about China and life along the Yangtze River.

Science • Study ducks.

Art • Make and decorate boats Ping may have lived on.

EXTENDED READING

Other Books by Marjorie Flack:
Angus and the Cat
Angus Lost
Ask Mr. Bear

Name _____

Draw a place you would hide if you were Ping.

I would hide _____

because _____

_____ .

Name _____

What do you think Ping would say to his family when he got back?

Name _____

Follow the directions and color the map of China.

1. Color **China** orange.
2. Color the **Pacific Ocean** blue.
3. Color the **U.S.S.R.** red.
4. Color the **Yangtze River** blue.

LEO THE LATE BLOOMER
Robert Kraus

BEFORE READING ACTIVITY
What are some things you couldn't do when you were younger but you can do now? (Discuss.)

This is a story about Leo who can't do some things either. See what happens to him.

AFTER READING ACTIVITY
How are you the same as Leo? How are you different? (List on board)

Same	Different
_____	_____
_____	_____
_____	_____

CRITICAL THINKING QUESTIONS
- When Leo becomes a father do you think he will worry if his children are late bloomers? Why, why not?
- What other things do you think Leo will be able to do later on?

THEMATIC/WHOLE LANGUAGE ACTIVITIES

Language Arts • Students read, write and draw things they once could not do. Keep in an "I Couldn't Then But I Can Now" folder for each child. Refer to it periodically to show the child's growth.

Social Studies • Discuss table manners and how to eat neatly.

Science • Learn about tigers and other jungle animals in the story.

EXTENDED READING
Other books by Robert Kraus:

Another Mouse to Feed
Boris Bad Enough
Buggy Bear Cleans Up
Bunnies Nutshell Library
Noel the Coward

Bumpy the Car
Freddie the Fire Engine
Happy Farm
How the Spider Saved Easter

Name _____

Draw the cover of a book you want Leo to read.

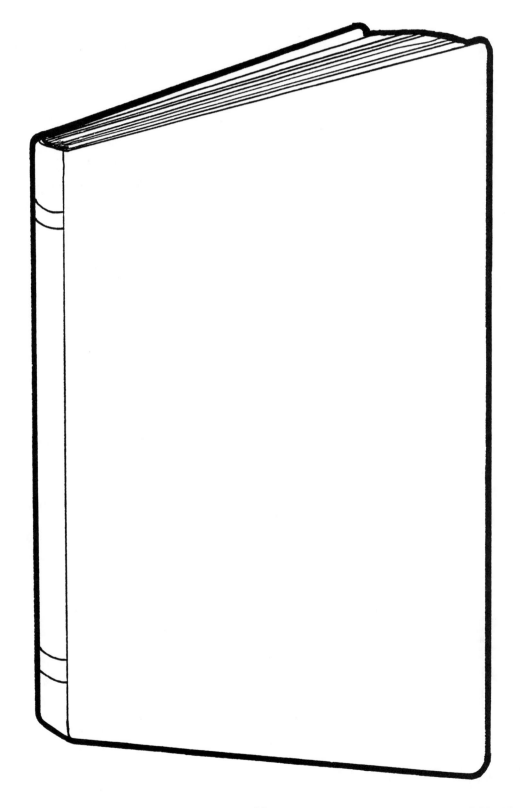

Leo the Late Bloomer

SOCIAL STUDIES:
Personal Awareness

Name _____

What are some things you can't do now but will do someday.

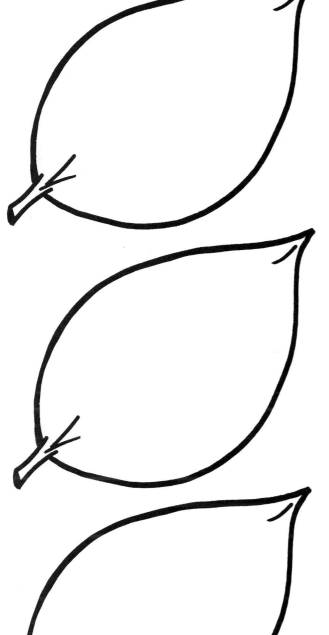

I can't _____

now, but someday I will.

I can't _____

now, but someday I will.

I can't _____

now, but someday I will.

T.S. Denison & Co., Inc.   25   *Launch Into Literature II*

Leo the Late Bloomer

Name _____

Write a letter to Leo telling how your are like him.

Dear Leo,

Your Friend,

CORDUROY
Don Freeman

BEFORE READING ACTIVITY

What does it mean to have a home? (Discuss.)

This is the story of a little bear named Corduroy who wants a home. See what happens.

AFTER READING ACTIVITY

How will Corduroy's life be different now that he's found a home and a friend? (Discuss.)

CRITICAL THINKING QUESTIONS

- Why do you think the girl didn't care if Corduroy had a button missing?
- Would you have chosen Corduroy to take home? Why, why not?
- What do you think happened to the button Corduroy found in the store?

THEMATIC/WHOLE LANGUAGE ACTIVITIES

Art
- Learn how to sew buttons on. Decorate pieces of fabric with them.

Language Arts
- Write a chart story about Corduroy's life with the little girl.

EXTENDED READING

Other books by Don Freeman:

Beady Bear	The Paper Party
Bearymore	A Pocket for Corduroy
Dandelion	A Rainbow of My Own
Hattie the Backstage Bat	Space Witch
Norman the Doorman	Tilly Witch

Name _____

Draw a stuffed toy that needs a home.

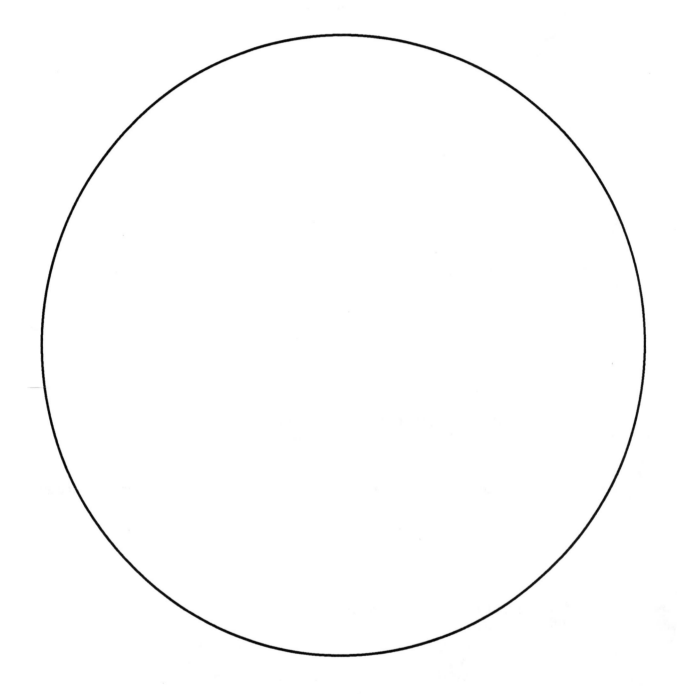

This is _____.

Corduroy

Name ———————————————————————————————

Color the Cordoroy puppet. Cut it out and put your fingers through for legs.
Put on a puppet show.

Name _____

Here is a button. Draw and write what it belongs to.

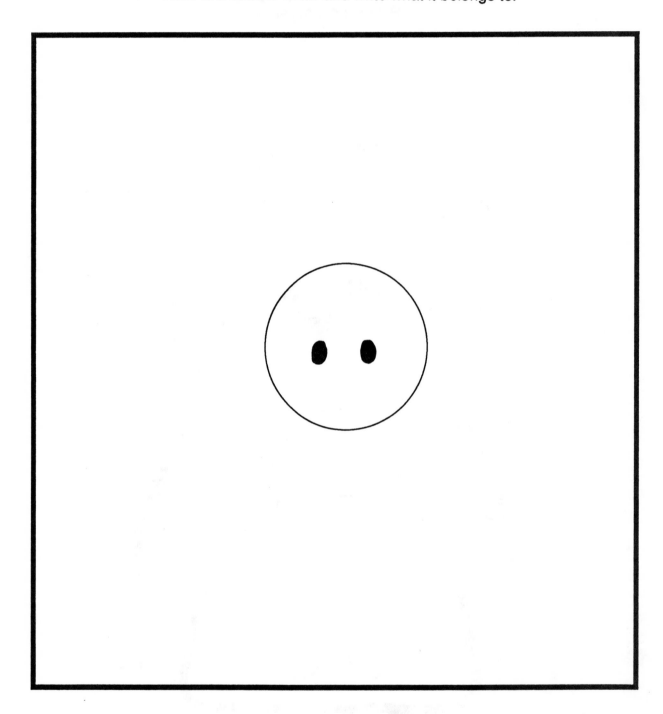

It belongs to_____

_____.

THE NAPPING HOUSE
Audrey Wood

BEFORE READING ACTIVITY
Who are the people and animals that sleep in your house? (List on board.)

Example:
mother	father
brother	sister
cat	dog

Let's see who is sleeping in this book.

AFTER READING ACTIVITY
Who were sleeping in the book? (Circle and list on board.)

Example:
mother	father	flea
brother	sister	granny
(cat)	(dog)	child

CRITICAL THINKING QUESTIONS
- What do you think kept the flea awake?
- Do you think the people in the book wanted to go back to sleep? Why, why not?

THEMATIC/WHOLE LANGUAGE ACTIVITIES

Science
- Study the need for sleep.
- Learn about pets (cats and dogs).

Social Studies
- Study how families are different. (That every family doesn't have a mother, father sister, brother.)

Language Arts
- Students write about who sleeps at their house and make their own "Napping House" book.

EXTENDED READING
Other books by Audrey Wood:
Quick as a Cricket
The Big Hungry Bear
King Bidgood's in the Bathtub

Name ——————————————————————

Draw all the people and animals on your cozy bed in your napping house.

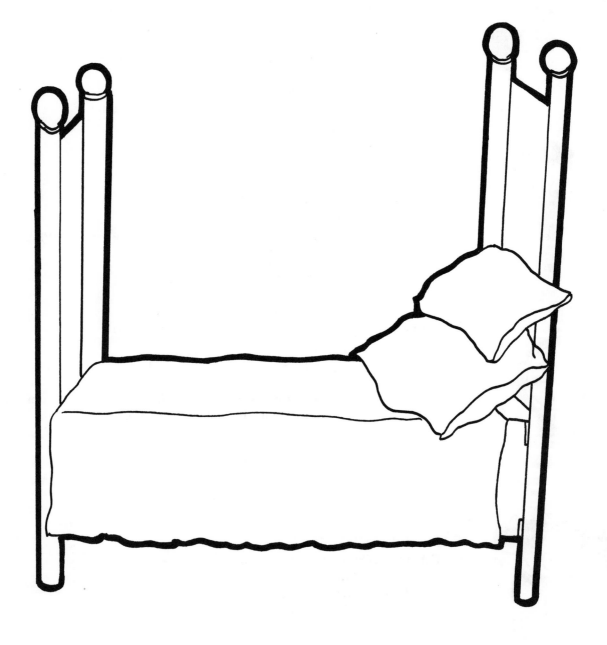

Name _____

Draw and write how the story would be different if the flea was asleep.

The flea was asleep.

Then _____

_____ .

Then _____

_____ .

Name _____

Write words that describe each person or animal. Draw each one.

_____granny

_____child

_____cat

_____dog

_____mouse

MAKE WAY FOR DUCKLINGS
Robert McCloskey

BEFORE READING ACTIVITY

Where do you think a perfect home for ducks would be? (Discuss.)

This is a story about Mr. and Mrs. Mallard and where they end up making their home.

AFTER READING ACTIVITY

How would the story be different if Mr. and Mrs. Mallard had chosen to live in the country? (Chain responses.)

Example:

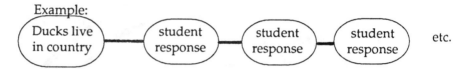

Ducks live in country — student response — student response — student response   etc.

CRITICAL THINKING QUESTIONS

- Do you think the ducklings will live in the park when they have a family? Why, why not?
- Will the ducks depend on people for all their food? Why, why not?

THEMATIC/WHOLE LANGUAGE ACTIVITIES

Social Studies	• Learn about city helpers like policemen.
Science	• Study ducks.
P.E.	• Play "Duck, Duck, Goose."

EXTENDED READING

Other Books by Robert McCloskey:
- *Centerbug Tales*
- *Homer Price*
- *Blueberries for Sal*
- *Time of Wonder*
- *Burt Dow; Deep Water Man*
- *Lentil*
- *One Morning in Maine*

Name _____

Follow the directions and color the map.

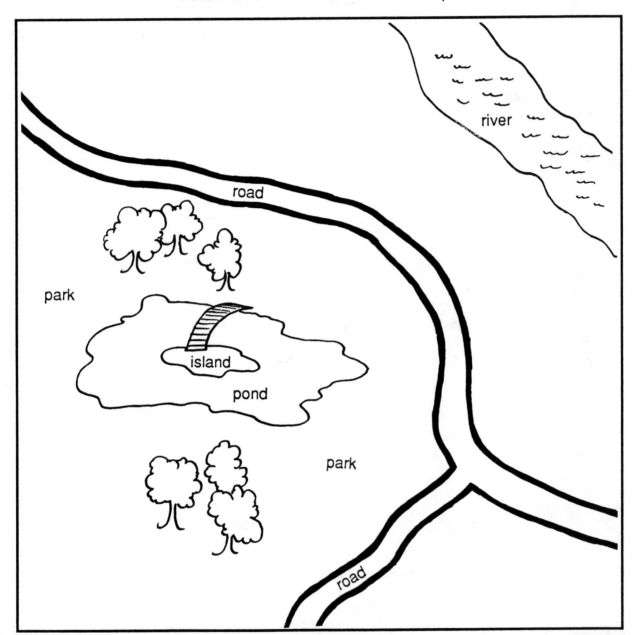

1. Color the roads **brown**.
2. Color the river **blue**.
3. Color the pond **blue**.
4. Color the island **green**.
5. Color the park **green**.
6. Draw where the ducks went from the
   river to the island. Use a **black** crayon.

Name _____

How is the duck family the same and different than your family?

Same   **Different**

_____   _____

_____   _____

_____   _____

_____   _____

Name _____

They should watch out for

_____

_____ .

They should watch out for

_____

_____ .

They should watch out for

_____

_____ .

KATY NO POCKETS
Emmy Payne

BEFORE READING ACTIVITY

What would you do if you didn't have any pockets? (List responses on board.)

Example: ask for help
solve it myself
cry
worry

In this story Katy has no pockets. See if she solves her problem like you would.

AFTER READING ACTIVITY

How did Katy go about solving her problem? (Circle and write responses.)

Example: (ask for help)
solve it myself
cry
(worry)
(think)
went to city

CRITICAL THINKING QUESTIONS

- How do you think the other animal mothers felt when Katy carried their children? Why?
- Do you think Freddy minds sharing his mother's pockets?
- How else could Katy have carried Freddy if she couldn't find pockets?

THEMATIC/WHOLE LANGUAGE ACTIVITIES

Science   • Learn about kangaroos.

Art   • Make pockets out of paper or cloth.

Math   • Graph the number of pockets each child is wearing
• Write what children are carrying in their pockets.

EXTENDED READING

Make Way for Ducklings – Robert McCloskey
Caps for Sale – Esphyr Slobadkina
Ira Sleeps Over – Bernard Waber

Name _____

Draw and label what you would put in these pockets.

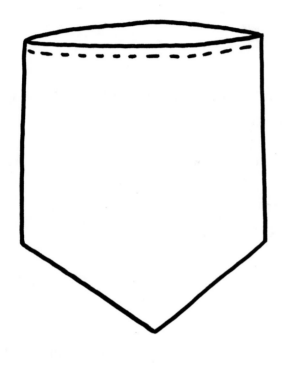 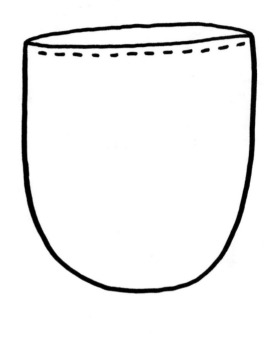

 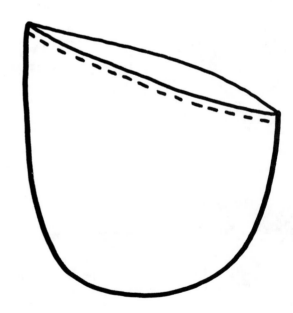

Name _____

What would have happened if Katy did not find any pockets?

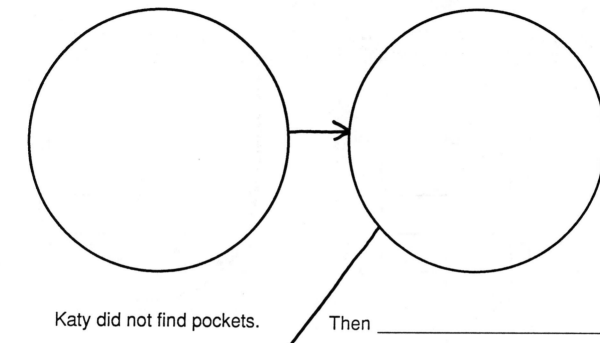

Katy did not find pockets.

Then _____

_____.

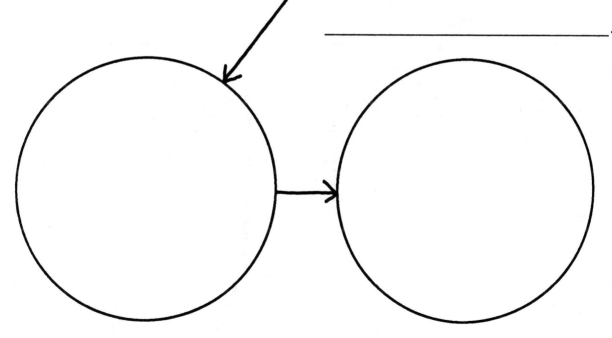

So _____

_____.

So _____

_____.

Katy No Pockets

Name _____

Graph the number of pockets children in your room have.

NUMBER OF POCKETS

	1	2	3	4	5	6	7+
1							
2							
3							
4							
5							
6							
7							
8							
9							
10							
11							
12							
13							
14							
15							

HARRY THE DIRTY DOG
Gene Zion

BEFORE READING ACTIVITY

What do you like about taking a bath? What don't you like? (Discuss.)

Harry is a dog who does not like baths. See what happens to him.

AFTER READING ACTIVITY

Do you think Harry has changed his mind about baths? Why or why not?

CRITICAL THINKING QUESTIONS
- Why do you think Harry hid the brush again at the end of the story?
- Would you have recognized Harry when he came back all dirty? Why, why not?

THEMATIC/WHOLE LANGUAGE ACTIVITIES

Health   • Discuss the importance of bathing and good grooming.

Science   • Learn how to take care of pets.

EXTENDED READING

Other books by Gene Zion:
Harry and the Lady Next Door
Harry By the Sea
No Roses for Harry

Name _____

Draw your pet or a pet you would like to have getting a bath.

He came home to get a bath.

He got dirtier and dirtier.

4.

3. fold #2

1.

2.

by:

Harry the Dirty Dog

Harry didn't like baths.
He ran away.

Name _____

Draw and write how you get dirty.

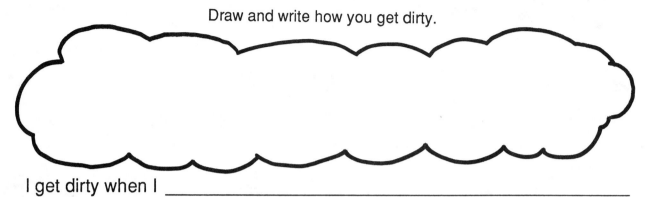

I get dirty when I _____

_____.

I get dirty when I _____

_____.

I get dirty when I _____

_____.

Teacher's Page
LITTLE TOOT
Hardie Gramatky

BEFORE READING ACTIVITY

What does it mean to work? What does it mean to play? (Discuss.)

In this story Little Toot learns the difference between the two.

AFTER READING ACTIVITY

How do you work? How do you play? (List and draw on board.)

Work	*Play*
_____	_____
_____	_____
_____	_____

CRITICAL THINKING QUESTIONS

- Why do you think Little Toot feels better about working than about playing?
- Do you think Little Toot will ever play again? Why, why not?

THEMATIC/WHOLE LANGUAGE ACTIVITIES

Language Arts • Write a chart story about other mighty deeds Little Toot did.

Science • Do experiments about what floats on water and what sinks.

Social Studies • Learn about the types of work people and boats do.

EXTENDED READING

The Little Engine That Could – Piper
Mike Mulligan and His Steam Shovel – Virginia Lee Burton
Katy and the Big Snow – Virginia Lee Burton

Name _____

Draw the kind of boat you would want to be. Write the name you would have.

My name would be _____

because _____.

Name _____

Design an award the people on the ocean liner might give Little Toot.

Name _____

How are you and Little Toot the same?
How are you different?

SAME   **DIFFERENT**

_____   _____

_____   _____

BREAD AND JAM FOR FRANCES
Russell Hoban

BEFORE READING ACTIVITY
What are your favorite foods? (List on board.)

Example: spaghetti   pizza
hamburger   cake
chicken

In this story Frances has some favorite foods too. See if they are the same as yours.

AFTER READING ACTIVITY
What foods did Frances eat in the story? (Circle responses, add others.)

Example: (spaghetti)   bread
pizza   jam
hamburger   carrot sticks
cake   celery
(chicken)

CRITICAL THINKING QUESTIONS
• How were Frances' parents smart?
• Would you like to eat the same thing all the time? Why, why not?
• Do you think Frances would like your favorite foods? Why, why not?

THEMATIC/WHOLE LANGUAGE ACTIVITIES
Science   • Study the four food groups.
• Have a tasting party to sample different foods.

Music   • Practice singing or reciting Frances' songs.
• Make up a class song.

P.E.   • Skip rope like Frances.

EXTENDED READING
Other books by Russell Hoban:
Baby Sister for Frances   *The Marzipan Pig*
Bedtime for Frances   *Mouse and His Child*
Bargain for Frances   *Nothing to Do*
A Birthday for Frances   *The Rain Door*

Name _____

Draw and write about your good lunch.

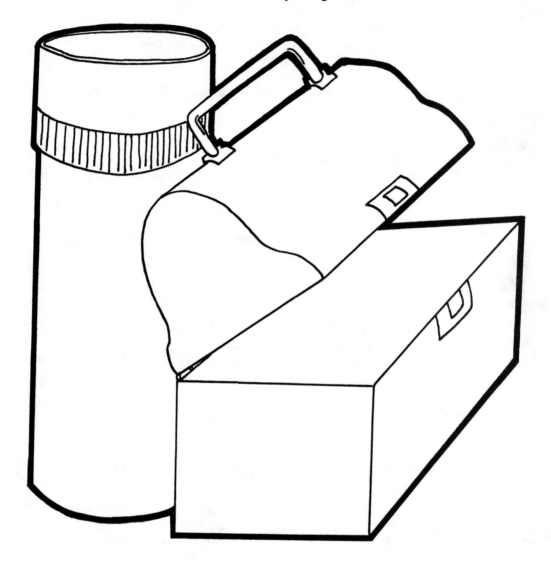

My good lunch is: _____

_____

_____

_____

_____

Name _____

How is Francis the same and different than you?

SAME	DIFFERENT

_____   _____

_____   _____

_____   _____

_____   _____

Name _____

Draw and make up a song about your favorite food.

My favorite food is _____.

_____

_____

_____

_____

KATY AND THE BIG SNOW
Virginia Lee Burton

BEFORE READING ACTIVITY
What does it feel like to work hard and help people? (List words on board.)

Example: good   happy
              tired   excited

This is the story about a snowplow named Katy who works hard and helps people. See if she feels the same as you.

AFTER READING ACTIVITY
How do you think Katy felt at the end of the day? (Circle responses, add others.)

Example: good   happy
              sleepy   sorry
              tired   excited

CRITICAL THINKING QUESTIONS
- What do you think happened to the broken down trucks?
- What would have happened if Katy was too tired to plow the whole city?

THEMATIC/WHOLE LANGUAGE ACTIVITIES

Social Studies   • Learn about city helpers and how cities work.
                     • Discuss how students can be good helpers.

Art   • Build a model city and draw maps of it.

Math   • Measure how deep the snow got in the story.

EXTENDED READING
Other books by Virginia Lee Burton:
   The Little House
   Calico, the Wonder Horse or The Saga of Stewy Slinker
   Mike Mulligan and His Steam Shovel
   Choo Choo

Name ───────────────────────

Write what Katy might say at the end of the day.

Name _____

Draw and write some ways you work hard and help people.

I work hard at

I work hard at

I work hard at

I work hard at

Katy and the Big Snow

Name _____

Follow the directions and color the map of Geoppolis.

1. Color the streets **brown**.
2. Color the school **yellow**.
3. Color the store **red**.
4. Color the library **blue**.
5. Color the park **green**.
6. Color the houses **orange**.

Teacher's Page
SPECTACLES
Ellen Raskin

BEFORE READING ACTIVITY

Have you ever had trouble seeing things? What kinds of problems do people who can't see well have? (Discuss.)

In this book Iris has some trouble seeing. Listen to see what happens.

AFTER READING ACTIVITY

How will life be better for Iris now that she can see? (Discuss.)

CRITICAL THINKING QUESTIONS

- How do you think people reacted to Iris before she got her glasses?
- How will they react to her now that she can see?
- Do you think anyone will make fun of her? Why, why not?

THEMATIC/WHOLE LANGUAGE ACTIVITIES

Art
- Draw or cut and pass things the way Iris saw them with and without her glasses.

Science
- Learn about the eye and the way glasses help people see.

EXTENDED READING

Other Books by Ellen Raskin:
> *Figgs and Phantoms*
> *Ghost in Four-Room Apartment*
> *Mysterious Disappearance of Leon (I mean Noel)*
> *Nothing Ever Happens on My Block*

Name _____

Decorate and cut out your own set of spectacles.

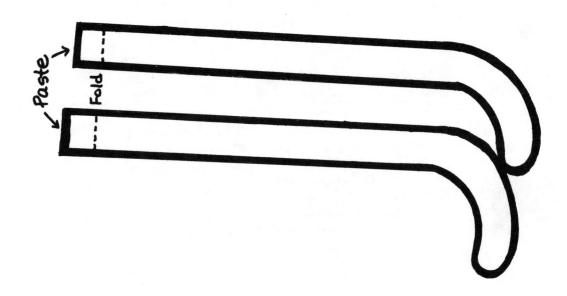

Name _____

Draw and write three ways glasses will help Iris.

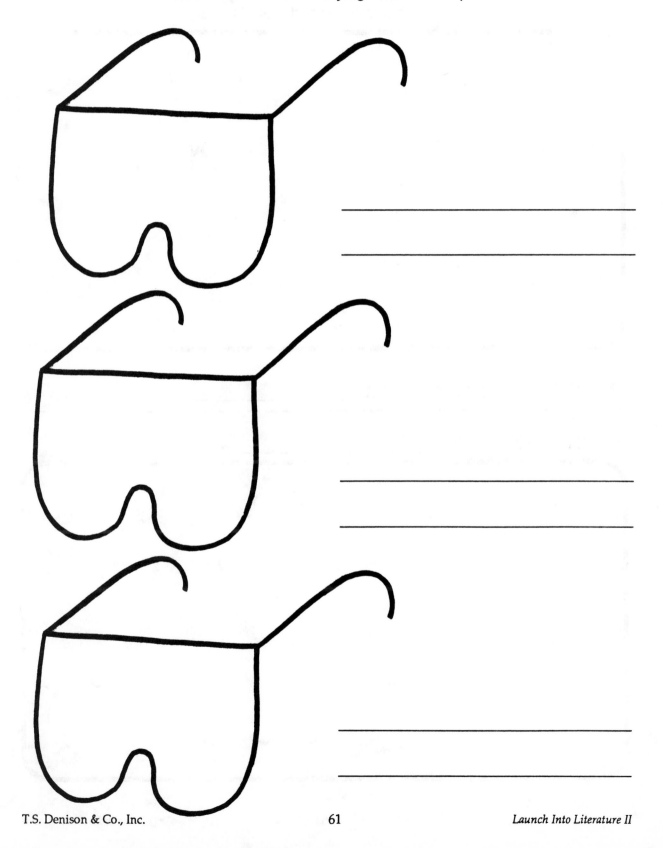

_____

_____

_____

_____

_____

_____

Name ——————————————————————————————————

Show what Iris sees without her glasses.
Then draw what it really is.

Without glasses Iris sees a _____.

It is really a _____.

Teacher's Page
IMOGENE'S ANTLERS
David Small

BEFORE READING ACTIVITY

What would you do if you woke up one morning to discover you had grown antlers? (Discuss.)

See what Imogene does about it.

AFTER READING ACTIVITY

What are some things that can be done with Imogene's peacock feathers? (List on board.)

CRITICAL THINKING QUESTIONS

• How do you think Imogene's mother will react to her peacock feathers?
• Will she be embarrassed if she has to go to school? Why, why not?

THEMATIC/WHOLE LANGUAGE ACTIVITIES

Science	• Learn about animals with antlers.
Language Arts	• Write a letter to Imogene about other uses for her antlers.

EXTENDED READING

Other books by David Small:
Eulalie and the Hopping Head
Paper John

Name _____

How do you think Imogene will look tomorrow when she wakes up?

I think she will have _____

_____ .

Name _____

What else can be done with Imogene's antlers?

They can be used for

_____

They can be used for

_____

They can be used for

_____

Name —————————————————————————

Design a way to cover Imogene's peacock feathers.

A CHAIR FOR MY MOTHER
Vera B. Williams

BEFORE READING ACTIVITY

Have you ever worked and saved money to buy something special? (Discuss.)

This story is about a girl and her family who save up to buy a chair.

AFTER READING ACTIVITY

What do you think they will save their money to buy next? (Discuss.)

CRITICAL THINKING QUESTIONS

- What jobs could you have done to earn money for the chair?
- What do you think they would have saved to buy if their house hadn't burned?
- Do you save your money or spend it? What's good or bad about savings? What's good or bad about spending?

THEMATIC/WHOLE LANGUAGE ACTIVITIES

Math	• Do money problems.
Science/Health	• Learn about fire safety.
Art	• Students decorate their classroom chairs.
P.E.	• Play musical chairs.

EXTENDED READING

Alfie Gives a Hand – Shirley Hughes
Earnest and Celestine – Gabrielle Vincent
Feelings – Aliki
Something Special for Me – Vera B. William

Name ———————————————————————————

Draw a chair you would like to have.

My chair has ———————————————————————

———————————————————————————.

Name _____

What would you save your money to buy?

I'd save my money to buy _____

because _____.

Name _____

How would you help a friend whose house burned down?

MIKE MULLIGAN AND HIS STEAM SHOVEL
Virginia Lee Burton

BEFORE READING ACTIVITY

What kinds of things do you think a steam shovel does? (Discuss.)

In this story Mike Mulligan and his steam shovel do a lot of projects. Listen to learn what they are.

AFTER READING ACTIVITY

What are some of the projects Mike Mulligan and Mary Anne did? (List on board.)

CRITICAL THINKING QUESTIONS
- How did Mike and Mary Anne help people with their digging?
- Do you think Mike Mulligan misses digging holes with Mary Anne? Why, why not?

THEMATIC/WHOLE LANGUAGE ACTIVITIES

Science • Do water experiments creating steam and showing its power.

Art • Make a mural of all the projects Mike and Mary Anne did.

EXTENDED READING

Other Books by Virginia Lee Burton
Katy and the Big Snow
The Little House
Life Story

Name _____

Draw a picture showing why this hole was dug.

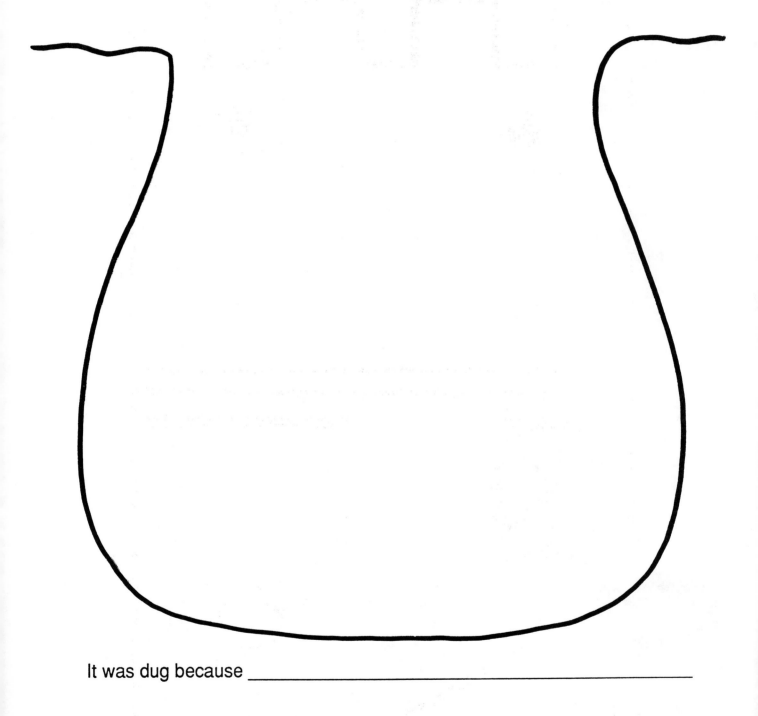

It was dug because _____

_____.

Name _____

Cut out Mike and Mary Anne. Paste them on a paper bag to make a puppet.
Do a puppet show.

Name _____

Draw another cover for this book.

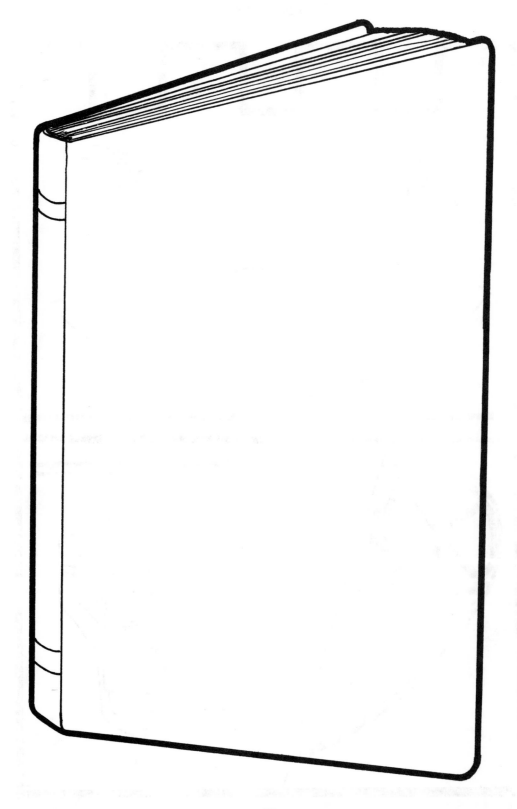

IF I RAN THE ZOO
Dr. Seuss

BEFORE READING ACTIVITY

What kinds of animals do you see in the zoo? (Discuss.)

This is the story of Gerald McGrew who would have different animals if he ran the zoo.

AFTER READING ACTIVITY

How are the animals in McGrew's Zoo the same and different than regular zoo animals? (List on board.)

Same	*Different*
_____	_____
_____	_____
_____	_____

CRITICAL THINKING QUESTIONS

- Why do you think Gerald McGrew wanted different animals in his zoo?
- Do you think he had trouble feeding the new animals? Why, why not?

THEMATIC/WHOLE LANGUAGE ACTIVITIES

Science • Learn about zoo animals.

Language Arts • Children make up names, diet, and places of origin of their original animals.

Art • Make a mural of the animals in your class's zoo.

EXTENDED READING

Other books by Dr. Seuss:

Horton Hatches the Egg
On Beyond Zebra
If I Ran the Circus
How the Grinch Stole Christmas
One Fish, Two Fish, Red Fish, Blue Fish
And to Think I Saw it on Mulberry Street
The 500 Hats of Bartholomew Cubbins
Yertle the Turtle and Other Stories

The Lorax
The Cat in the Hat
Green Eggs and Ham
Horton Hears a Who

Name _____

Write a poem about an animal in your own zoo. Draw a picture to go with it.

_____
your animal's name

_____

_____

_____

_____

Name _____

Draw the place your animal comes from.

My animal comes from _____

_____ .

Name _____

What do you think happened when all the regular zoo animals were let go?

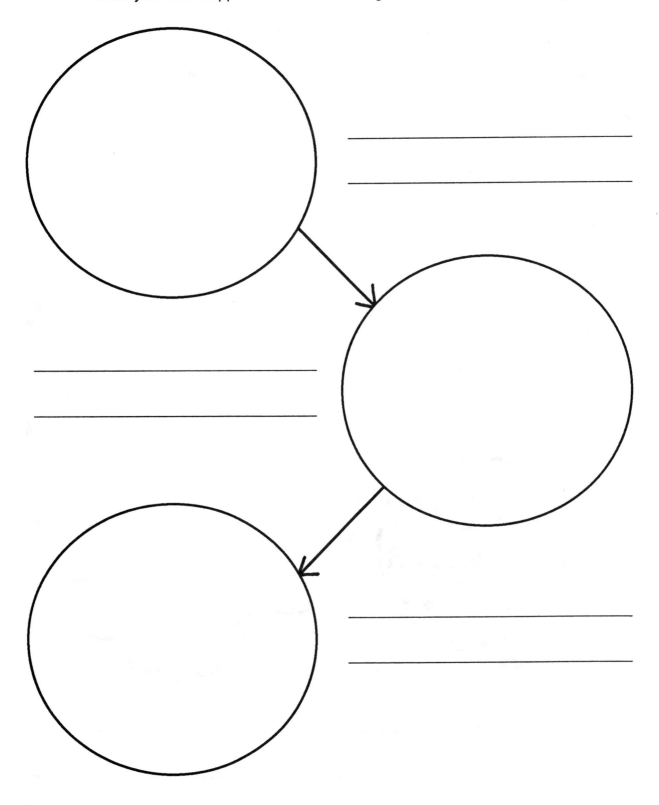

ALEXANDER AND THE WIND-UP MOUSE
Leo Lionni

BEFORE READING ACTIVITY

Have you ever wanted to be like someone else? (Discuss.)

In this story Alexander wants to be like his friend Willy, a wind-up mouse. Listen to what happens.

AFTER READING ACTIVITY

Chaining: How would the story be different if Alexander became a wind-up mouse?

Example:

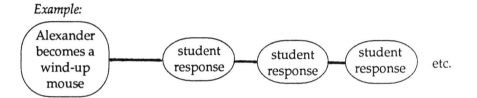

Alexander becomes a wind-up mouse — student response — student response — student response etc.

CRITICAL THINKING QUESTIONS

- Do you think Alexander made the right decision? Why, why not?
- How do you think Willy feels?

THEMATIC/WHOLE LANGUAGE ACTIVITIES

Science   • Study rocks. Look for pebbles of every color.

Art   • Make torn paper mice like the illustration in the book.

Language Arts   • Write stories about wishes.

EXTENDED READING

Other books by Leo Lionni:
The Biggest House in the World
Fish is Fish
Frederick
Swimming
Tico and the Golden Wings

Name _____

How are Alexander and the wind-up mouse the same and different?

SAME	**DIFFERENT**

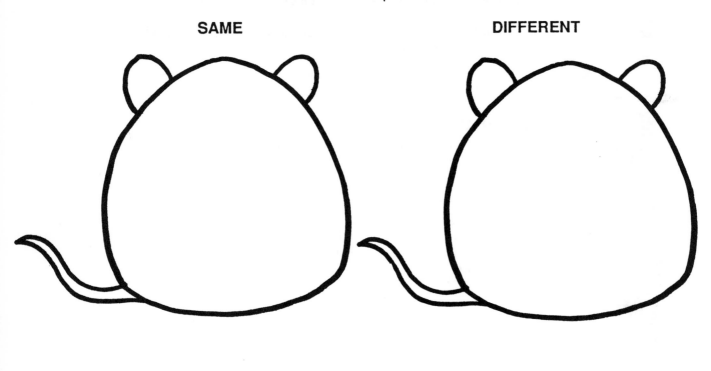

_____   _____

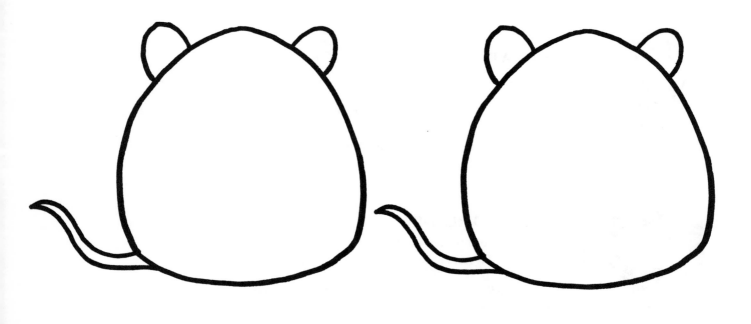

_____   _____

Name _____

What would you have wished for with the purple pebble?

I would wish for _____

_____.

Name _____

What would have happened if Alexander wished he was a wind-up mouse?

_____ Alexander becomes _____

_____ a wind-up mouse. _____

THE TENTH GOOD THING ABOUT BARNEY
Judith Viorst

BEFORE READING ACTIVITY
Have you ever had a pet die? How did it feel? What did you do? (List on board.)

Example:

cry	get mad
feel lonely	wasn't hungry

In this story Barney the cat is dead. See how people feel about it.

AFTER READING ACTIVITY
How did the boy in the story act (Circle responses, add others.)

Example:

cry (circled)	missed Barney
get mad	had funeral
feel lonely (circled)	didn't watch T.V.
wasn't hungry (circled)	planted seeds

CRITICAL THINKING QUESTIONS
• Do you think they will get another pet? Why, why not?
• Did the mother and father help the child? How?

THEMATIC/WHOLE LANGUAGE ACTIVITIES
Social Studies   • Talk about death and what it means.

Science   • Grow seeds.
           • Study soil.

EXTENDED READING
Other books by Judith Viorst:
Sunday Morning
Rosie and Michael
Alexander Who Used to Be Rich Last Sunday
Alexander and the Terrible, Horrible, No Good, Very Bad Day
I'll Fix Anthony
The Good-Bye Book
If I Were in Charge of the World and Other Worries

Name _____

Draw your pet or a pet you would like to have. Write ten good things about them.

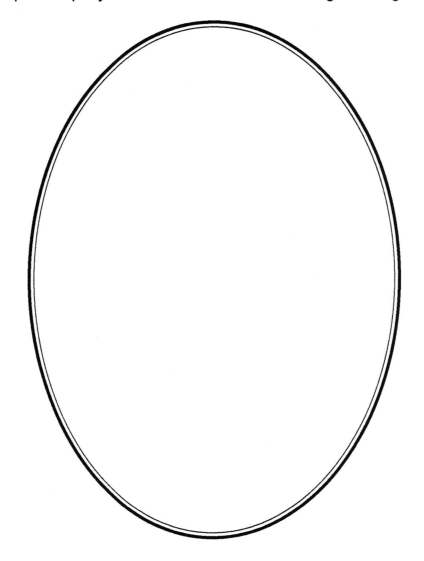

1. _____   6. _____

2. _____   7. _____

3. _____   8. _____

4. _____   9. _____

5. _____   10. _____

Name _____

What do you think happened after the end of the story?

Name _____

Where do you think animals go when they die?

I think animals go _____

because _____

_____.

AMELIA BEDELIA
Peggy Parish

BEFORE READING ACTIVITY

Have you ever misunderstood directions before? (Discuss.)

Amelia Bedelia was given some interesting directions in this book. See what she does.

AFTER READING ACTIVITY

What do you think would happen if Amelia didn't make the pie?

CRITICAL THINKING QUESTIONS

- Do you think Amelia was trying to be silly? Why, why not?
- Will Amelia be able to follow directions better in the future? Why, why not?

THEMATIC/WHOLE LANGUAGE ACTIVITIES

Language Arts   • Make silly lists for Amelia to follow then rewrite them so they make sense.

Art   • Do a bulletin board on Amelia Bedelia.

EXTENDED READING

Other Books by Peggy Parish:
Thank you, Amelia Bedelia
Amelia Bedelia and the Surprise Shower
Come Back, Amelia Bedelia
Play Ball, Amelia Bedelia

Amelia Bedelia

Name _____

Do these things:

1. Measure these cups of rice:

 =

2. Draw these drapes:

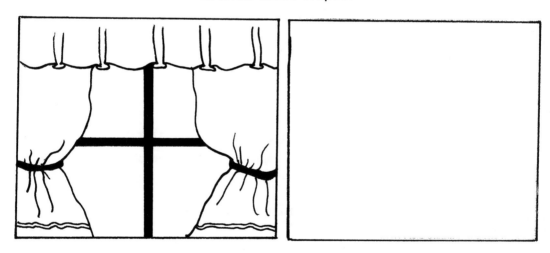

3. Dress this chicken:

Amelia Bedelia

Name _____

Read the list for Amelia Bedelia. Draw what she will do.

List

1. Dust the rug.

2. Make jelly rolls.

3. Change the bed.

1.

Amelia Bedelia will

_____

_____.

2.

Then she will

_____

_____.

3.

Last she will

_____

_____.

Name _____

LEMON PIE

1. Mix together until thick:

   2 cups sweetened condensed milk (15 oz.)
   1/3 cup lemon juice
   1 Tbsp. grated lemon rind
   1/4 tsp. salt

2. Blend in:

   2/3 cup drained canned pineapple

3. Put in a cooked pie shell.

4. Chill for three hours.

- -

Draw the four steps to this recipe.

1.	2.
3.	4.

CLOUDY WITH A CHANCE OF MEATBALLS
Judi Barrett

BEFORE READING ACTIVITY
Would you like to live in a place where things are very different? Why, why not? (Discuss.)

This is a story about a town where the weather is *very* different!

AFTER READING ACTIVITY
What were the good things about living in Chewandswallow?
What were the bad things? (List on board.)

Good Things	*Bad Things*
_____	_____
_____	_____
_____	_____

CRITICAL THINKING QUESTIONS
- What do you think happened at Chewandswallow once everyone was gone?
- Would you want to live there? Why, why not?
- What do you think would have happened if everyone stayed in Chewandswallow?

THEMATIC/WHILE LANGUAGE ACTIVITIES

Science	• Study weather.
	• Learn about the four food groups.
Language Arts	• Write a class book about strange weather.
Math	• (Measuring) Cook one of the things that may have landed in Chewandswallow.

EXTENDED READING
Other books by Judi Barrett:
Animals Should Definitely not Act Like People
Animals Should Definitely Not Wear Clothing
Benjamin's 365 Birthdays
Old McDonald Had an Apartment House

Name _____

Draw your favorite foods raining from the sky.
Write what they are.

It is raining _____

_____.

Name _____

Draw the raft you would build out of food.
Write what it is made of.

My raft is made of _____

_____.

Name _____

Write a newspaper article about the bad storm hitting Chewandswallow.

First Edition	**The Chewandswallow Digest**	Still Only 25¢

_____
(headline)

(picture)

_____

_____

_____

_____

_____

_____

THE WEDNESDAY SURPRISE
Eve Bunting

BEFORE READING ACTIVITY

Have you ever prepared a surprise for someone? What did it feel like?

In this book Grandma and Anna are putting together a surprise for Dad's birthday.

AFTER READING ACTIVITY

How would the story have been different if Anna had learned to read instead of Grandma?

CRITICAL THINKING QUESTIONS

- How do you think Grandma felt about herself when she couldn't read? How do you think she feels about herself now?

THEMATIC/WHOLE LANGUAGE ACTIVITIES

Language Arts
- Students write stories that other's read.
- Institute "partner reading" when children read to one another.

Social Studies
- Discuss different family groupings.

Art
- Make a book jacket for a favorite book.

EXTENDED READING

Another book by Eve Bunting:
Ghost's Hour, Spook's Hour

Name ———————————————————————————

Draw the cover of a book you like to read.

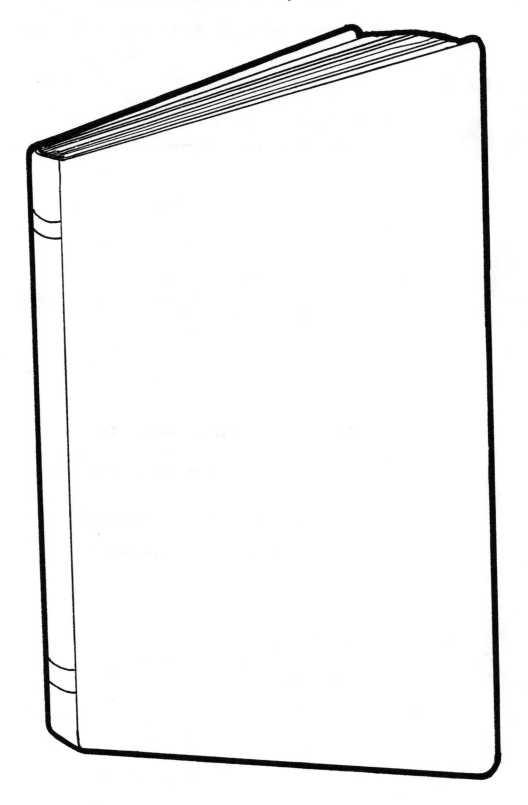

Name _____

Draw and write a present you would give to Grandma.

I would give her _____

because _____

_____ .

Name —————————————————————————

Write a letter to Anna from Grandma about the surprise.

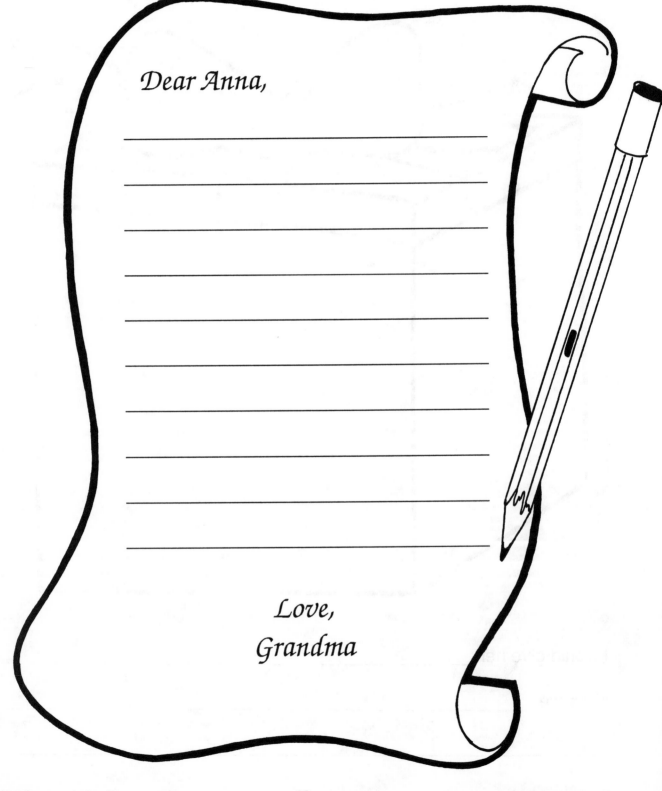

Dear Anna,

—————————————————————

—————————————————————

—————————————————————

—————————————————————

—————————————————————

—————————————————————

—————————————————————

—————————————————————

—————————————————————

Love,
Grandma

WHY MOSQUITOES BUZZ IN PEOPLE'S EARS
Verna Aardema

BEFORE READING ACTIVITY
Have you ever had a mosquito buzz in your ear?

This is a folktale about why mosquitoes do that.

AFTER READING ACTIVITY
Chaining: What do you think would have happened if the mosquito went to the council to face the lion?

Example:

Mosquito went to lion — student response — student response — student response   etc.

CRITICAL THINKING QUESTIONS
• Why do you think the mosquito told the iguana a lie in the first place?
• How would the story be different if the owl's child wasn't killed?

THEMATIC/WHOLE LANGUAGE ACTIVITIES
Art

• Experiment painting and drawing African-like prints similar to the story's illustrations.

Language Arts

• Make up stories about how other insects got their habits.

EXTENDED READING
Another book by Verna Aardema:

Who's in Rabbit's House

Other interesting books:

Where's My hippopotamus? – Mark Alan Stamaty

A Wart Snake in a Fig Tree – George Mendoza

The Ring in the Prairie – John Bierhorst

Name _____

Draw what the animals do at night. Draw what they do in the day.

NIGHT

At night they _____

_____.

DAY

During the day they _____

_____.

Name _____

Which was your favorite animal in the story? Why?

I like the _____because

_____

_____.

Name _____

What do you think would have happened if the mosquito had gone to the council meeting?

FROG AND TOAD ALL YEAR
Arnold Lobel

BEFORE READING ACTIVITY

Do you have a friend you do a lot of things with (Discuss.)

Frog and Toad are friends. See what they do together all year long.

AFTER READING ACTIVITY

How are Frog and Toad like you and your special friend?
How are they different? (List on board.)

Same	*Different*
_____	_____
_____	_____
_____	_____

CRITICAL THINKING QUESTIONS

- How can you tell Frog and toad are friends
- Do you think Spring is around a real corner like Frog says? Why, why not?

THEMATIC/WHOLE LANGUAGE ACTIVITIES

Science	• Study the seasons and weather.
Social Studies	• Learn about different celebrations and holidays throughout the year.
Language Arts	• Make ice cream and write a chart story about it.

EXTENDED READING

Other Books by Arnold Lobel:

Frog and Toad are Friends	*Grasshopper on the Road*
Days with Frog and Toad	*Ming Lo Loves the Mountain*
Frog and Toad Coloring Book	*Frog and Toad Pop-Up Book*
Frog and Toad Together	*The Book of Pigericks*
Owl At Home	*Mouse Soup*
Mouse Tales	*Fables*
On the Day Peter Stuyvesant Sailed into Town	

Name _____

Draw and write the things you like to do in winter.

I like to _____

_____.

I like to _____

_____.

I like to _____

_____.

Use after reading – *Down the Hill*

Name _____

Draw winter and spring. How are they different?

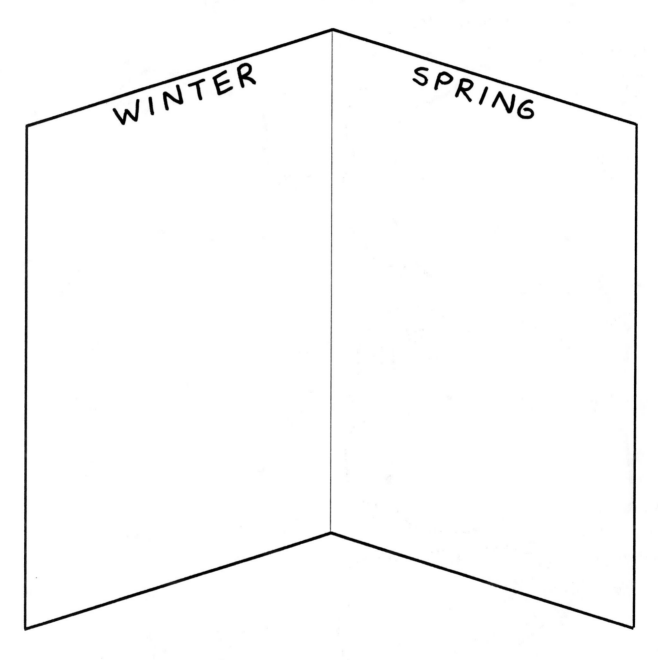

Winter and spring are different because _____

_____

_____.

Use after reading – *The Corner*

Name ——————————————————————

Where are good and bad places to eat ice cream?

GOOD   **BAD**

Use after reading - *Ice Cream*

Name _____

What are some ways you can surprise your friends?

I can _____

_____ .

I can _____

_____ .

I can _____

_____ .

ART/LANGUAGE ARTS:
Creative Expression

Name _____

What present would you give Toad?
What present would you give Frog?

I would give Frog _____

_____ .

I would give Toad _____

_____ .

A LION TO GUARD US
Clyde Robert Bulla

BEFORE READING ACTIVITY
Have you ever had a special good-luck charm that protected you? What was it? (Discuss.)

This is the story of three children whose father gave them something special to guard them. See if it works.

AFTER READING ACTIVITY
How would the story have been different if the children had lost the lion's head? (Chain responses on board.)

Example:

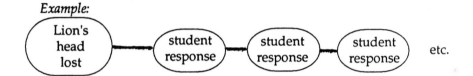

Lion's head lost — student response — student response — student response — etc.

CRITICAL THINKING QUESTIONS
- Do you think there was ever a time Amanda thought they would not make it?
- Which character is most like you? Which is least like you? How?
- What do you think happened to the two men left back on Bermuda?

THEMATIC/WHOLE LANGUAGE ACTIVITIES
Social Studies
- Learn about the Jamestown colony.
- Make a map of Bermuda complete with houses and everything mentioned in the book.

Languages Arts
- Students keep a journal depicting the adventures of the trip from character's point of view. (For younger children this can be done as a daily whole group chart story).

EXTENDED READING
Other books by Clyde Robert Bulla:
Daniel's Duck
Shoeshine Girl

Name _____

Draw a special thing you would want to guard you and keep you safe. Describe it.

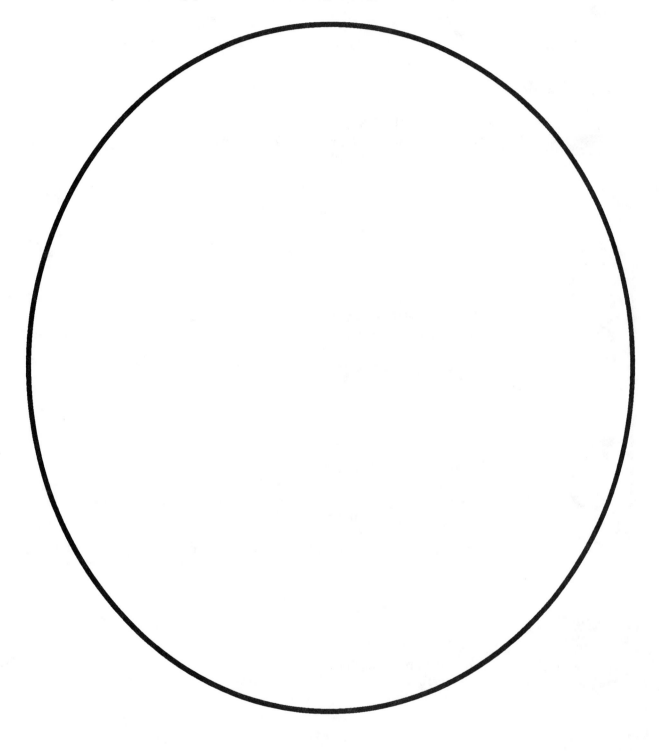

It is a _____.

Use after reading chapter 2 – *A Story*

Name _____

Draw and write where you would stay if you had no home.

I would stay _____

_____.

Use after reading chapter 7 – *Night People*

Name _____

What would you pack in your sea chest to go to America?

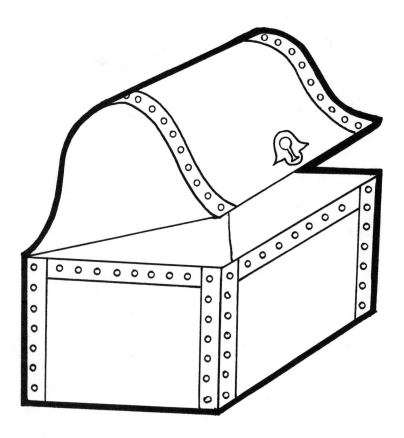

I would pack _____

_____

_____

_____

_____ .

Use after reading chapter 10 – *The Sea Adventure*

ART/LANGUAGE ARTS:
Analytic Thinking

Name _____

What would you be hungry for on the island?

I would be hungry for _____

_____

_____

_____.

Use after reading chapter 17 – *The Island*

Name ───────────────────────────────

Follow the directions and color the map.

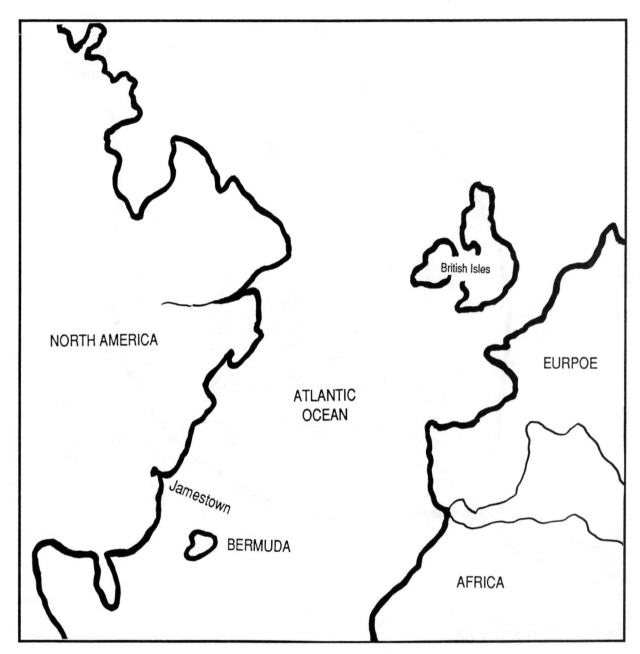

1. Color the British Isles **green**.
2. Color North America **red**.
3. Color Bermuda **yellow**.
4. Color the atlantic Ocean **blue**.
5. Draw the ships route from London to Bermuda to Jamestown.

Use after book is finished.

THE DRINKING GOURD
F.N. Monjo

BEFORE READING ACTIVITY

Have you ever done something other people said was wrong but you knew was right? (Discuss.)

In this story Tommy has to make a decision like that. See what he does.

AFTER READING ACTIVITY

How was Tommy brave? How was he a pest? (List on board.)

Example:

Brave	*Pest*
_____	_____
_____	_____
_____	_____

CRITICAL THINKING QUESTIONS

- Do you agree with Tommy and his father about helping runaway slaves? Why, why not?
- Do you think the Marshall will ever catch Tommy and his father? Why, why not?
- Will Tommy's pesty behavior change? Why, why not?

THEMATIC/WHOLE LANGUAGE ACTIVITIES

Social Studies	• Learn more about the underground railroad.
Science	• Study constellations.
Language Arts	• Write journals (or a chart story) about Little Jeff and the experience he had getting to Canada.

EXTENDED READING

Other books by F.N. Mongo:
Indian Summer
One Bad Thing About Father

Name _____

Draw a picture around the stars to make it look like a big dipper or a drinking gourd.

Use after reading chapter 2 – *The Runaways*

The Drinking Gourd

Name _____

Follow the directions and color the map of the Underground Railroad.

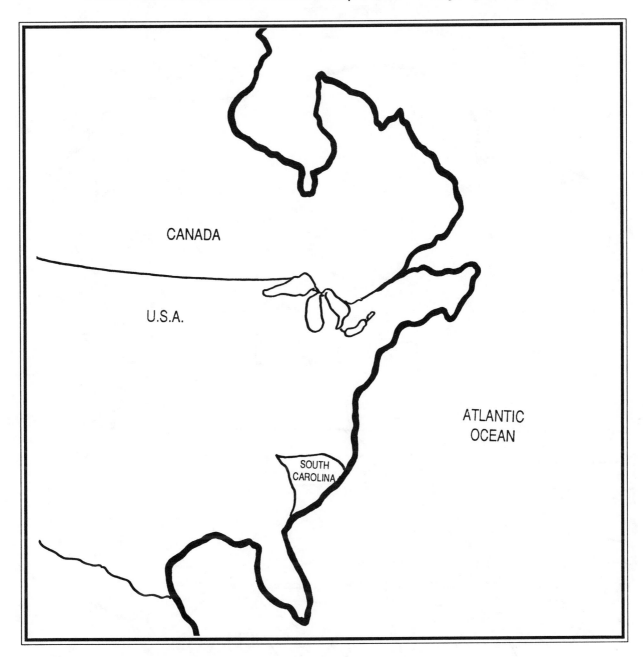

1. Color Canada **red**.
2. Color South Carolina **yellow**.
3. Color the rest of the U.S.A. **green**.
4. Color the Atlantic Ocean **blue**.
4. Use a **black** crayon. Draw a line from South Carolina into Canada to show Little Jeff's road to freedom.

Use after reading chapter 3 – *The Underground Railroad*

Name _____

Make up a story you would have told if you were Tommy.

Use after reading chapter 4 – *The Searching Party*

Name _____

What would have happened if Little Jeff's family was caught?

Little Jeff's

family is caught.

Name _____

Write a letter to Tommy as if you were Little Jeff.

Dear Tommy,

_____

_____

_____

_____

_____

_____

_____

_____

Your Friend,
Little Jeff

Use after book is finished.

HELP! I'M A PRISONER IN THE LIBRARY
Eth Clifford

BEFORE READING ACTIVITY

How are things scary in the dark but not scary in daylight? (Discuss.)

This is the story about two sisters who spend the night in a library. See if they are scared of things you would be.

AFTER READING ACTIVITY

How was the library scary? How was it interesting? (List responses on board.)

Scary	*Interesting*
_____	_____
_____	_____
_____	_____

CRITICAL THINKING QUESTIONS

- If you were in the library would you have dressed up in the old clothes? Why, why not?
- Who do you know who is like Miss Finton? Explain.
- When have you thought you heard a Banshee?

THEMATIC/WHOLE LANGUAGE ACTIVITIES

Health	• Learn about some basic first aid procedures like those mentioned in the book.
Language Arts	• Decipher the meaning of sayings the librarian used. Think of other sayings.
Art/Language Arts	• Students construct a fortune teller box. Write fortunes on pieces of paper, mix them up and distribute them through the fortune teller.

EXTENDED READING

Classic storybook titles:
> *The Wizard of Oz*
> *The Three Bears*
> *The Little Mermaid*
> *Snow White*
> *Sleeping Beauty*

Name _____

Write and decorate a sign you would put in the library window.

Help! I'm a Prisioner in the Library

LANGUAGE ARTS:
Creative Writing

Name _____

If you had a mynah bird what five things would you teach it to say?

Use after reading – *We Weren't Dead*

1. " _____

_____ ."

2. " _____

_____ ."

3. " _____

_____ ."

4. " _____

_____ ."

5. " _____

_____ ."

Help! I'm a Prisioner in the Library

ART/LANGUAGE ARTS:
Creative Expression

Name _____

Draw your own fortune teller and write your fortune.

Fortune
1 ¢ Told

YOUR FORTUNE IS

_____

_____

_____

_____

Use after reading – *Madam Morgana Sees and Hears All*

Help! I'm a Prisoner in the Library

ART:
Analytical Thinking

Name _____

Draw and label the books and displays you would put in your own storybook museum.

BOOKS

_____

_____

_____

_____

DISPLAYS

_____

_____

_____

_____

Use after reading – *Black the Boots and Make Them Shine*

Help! I'm a Prisoner in the Library

LANGUAGE ARTS:
Expository Writing

Name _____

Write and draw a T.V. report about the girls being found in the library.

Use after book is finished.

FRECKLE JUICE
Judy Blume

BEFORE READING ACTIVITY
Is there something about your looks that you do not like? What are they?

Andrew has that same problem in this story. See how he tries to solve it.

AFTER READING ACTIVITY
How would the story have been different if the freckle juice really worked? (Chain responses on board.)

Example:

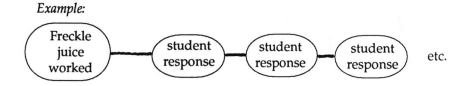

Freckle juice worked — student response — student response — student response   etc.

CRITICAL THINKING QUESTIONS
- Do you think Mrs. Kelly likes Andrew? Why, why not?
- How would you get even with Sharon?
- Should Nicky feel bad that he has freckles? Why, why not?

THEMATIC/WHOLE LANGUAGE ACTIVITIES

Social Studies   • Learn about similarities and differences in the way people look and act.

Math   • Graph characteristics of students in class.

Example:

	1	2	3	4	5	6	7	8	9	10	etc.
freckles											
dark hair											
light hair											
boy											
girl											
etc.											

EXTENDED READING
Other books by Judy Blume:

Tales of a Fourth Grade Nothing	*Blubber*
The Pair and the Great One	*Superfudge*
Otherwise Known as Sheila the Great	*Iggie's House*
The One in the Middle is the Green Kangaroo	

Name _____

Put 86 freckles on this face.

Use after reading chapter 1

Name _____

Graph the people in your class with freckles.

	FRECKLES	NO FRECKLES
1.		
2.		
3.		
4.		
5.		
6.		
7.		
8.		
9.		
10.		
11.		
13.		
14.		
15.		

How many people in your class have freckles? _____

How many do not have freckles? _____

Do you have freckles? _____

Use after reading chapter 2

Name _____

Make up your own recipe for freckle juice.

Freckle Juice

Use after reading chapter 3

Freckle Juice

Name _____

What would you do if you were Andrew and had to go to school?

First I would _____

_____

_____.

Then I would _____

_____

_____.

The last thing I would _____

_____

_____.

Use after chapter 4

Name _____

What do you think Nicky did after the end of the story
when he asked Sharon for some freckle juice.

_____   _____

Nicky asked Sharon

_____   _____

for Freckle juice.

_____   _____

Use after reading chapter 5

FANTASTIC MR. FOX
Roald Dahl

BEFORE READING ACTIVITY

Have you ever been faced with a difficult problem? How did you solve it? (Discuss.)

In this book Mr. Fox is faced with a terrible problem. See how he solves it.

AFTER READING ACTIVITY

How was Mr. Fox's solution fantastic and how was it lucky? (List on board.)

Fantastic	Lucky
_____	_____
_____	_____
_____	_____

CRITICAL THINKING QUESTIONS

- What would have happened if Mr. Fox never found any of the farms with his tunnels?
- How does the fox family feel about each other? How can you tell?
- Do you think any of the farmers changed after their experiences in this story? Why, why not?

THEMATIC/WHOLE LANGUAGE ACTIVITIES

Art
- Construct a diarama of Mr. Fox's hole.

Science
- Study the fox and other animals in the story.
- Have a tasting party and taste duck, chicken, turkey, ham, bacon and compare the flavors.

Music
- Sing "The Fox Went Out on a Chilly Night."

EXTENDED READING

Other books by Roald Dahl:

Charlie and the Chocolate Factory	Dirty Beasts
Charlie and the Glass Elevator	The BFG
The Wonderful Story of Henry Sugar	Magic Finger
Danny the Champion of the World	Mathilda
James and the Giant Peach	The Witches
The Enormous Crocodile	Boy Tales of Childhood
George's Marvelous Medicine	The Giraffe and Pelly and Me

Fantastic Mr. Fox

Name ————————————————————————————————

What other disgusting things might a friend of the farmers eat? Draw and describe it.

He would eat

————————————————————————————

————————————————————————————

————————————————————————————

Use after chapter 1 – *The Three Farmers*

Name _____

What would you do if your were Mr. Fox and your family began to starve?

I would _____

_____.

Use after reading chapter 8 – *The Foxes Begin to Starve*

Name _____

What other things would you want to eat at a feast if you were Mrs. Fox?

I would want to eat

_____

_____

and _____

_____

and _____

_____

Use after reading chapter 11 – *A Surprise for Mrs. Fox*

Name ______________________________

Make up a poem about someone in the story.

____

____

____

____

____

____

Draw them here.

Use after chapter 17 – *The Great Feast*

Name _____

What do you think happened to Mr. Fox and the farmers after the story ended?

Use after book is finished.

THE MOUSE AND THE MOTORCYCLE
Beverly Cleary

BEFORE READING ACTIVITY

Have you ever wanted to grow up real fast? What kind of things do you think you could do being a grown up? (Discuss.)

This is the story of a boy, a mouse, and a motorcycle and how they grow up a little.

AFTER READING ACTIVITY

What kinds of things did Keith and Ralph do to show they grew up a little? (List responses on board.)

Keith	Ralph
_____	_____
_____	_____
_____	_____

CRITICAL THINKING QUESTIONS

- If you were Keith would you have been as understanding when Ralph lost the motorcycle?
- What other kind of "tip" do you think the mouse family could have given Keith?
- Do you think the maids tried to poison the mice? Why, why not?

THEMATIC/WHOLE LANGUAGE ACTIVITIES

Science • Learn about mice.

Social Studies • Plot Keith's trip from Ohio to San Francisco and back.
• Discuss responsibility and ways the students are already responsible.

EXTENDED READING

Other books by Beverly Cleary include:

Henry Huggins   *Beezus and Ramona*
Ellen Tesbbits   *Henry and Beezus*
Ramona and Her Father   *Dear Mr. Henshaw*
Socks

Name _____

Draw and label what you would put into the wastebasket to help Ralph get out.

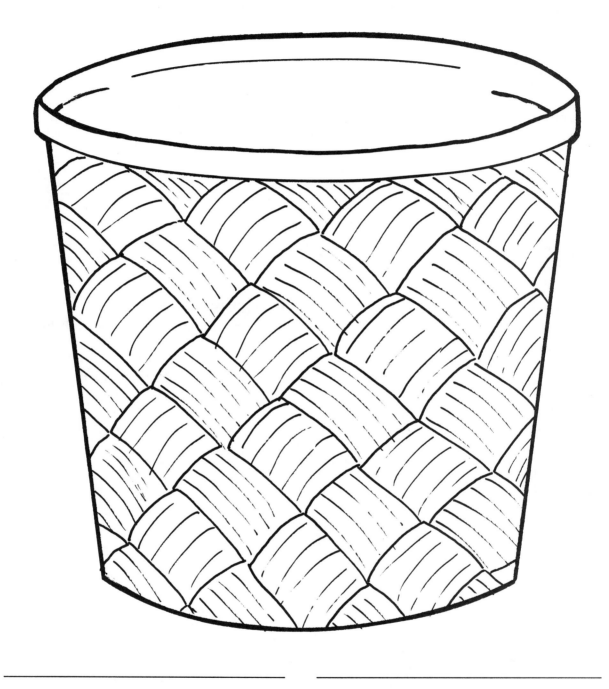

_____   _____

_____   _____

_____   _____

Use after reading chapter 4 – *Trapped*

ART/LANGUAGE ARTS:
Creative Expression

The Mouse and the Motorcycle

Name ______________________________

If you were Ralph, where would you want to ride the motorcycle?

____

____

____

____

____

____

Read after reading chapter 5 – *Adventure in the Night*

Name _____

What feast would you bring Ralph and his family to eat?
Draw and write them.

I would bring them

_____

_____

_____

_____

Use after reading chapter 8 – *A Family Reunion*

Name _____

What would you have done with Ralph if you were the school teachers?
Draw and write your answer.

I would _____

_____

_____.

Use after reading chapter 11 – *The Search*

Name _____

How are Ralph and Keith the same? How are they different?

SAME

_____   _____

_____   _____

DIFFERENT

_____   _____

_____   _____

Use after the book is finished.

MR. POPPER'S PENGUINS
Richard and Florence Atwater

BEFORE READING ACTIVITY

Have you ever dreamed about going someplace special? Did it ever happen? (Discuss.)

This is the story of Mr. Popper who dreamed of traveling to exotic places. See if his dream comes true.

AFTER READING ACTIVITY

What do you think would have happened if Mr. Popper had put the penguins in the movies? (Chain responses on board.)

Example:

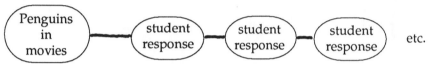

Penguins in movies — student response — student response — student response — etc.

CRITICAL THINKING QUESTIONS

- Do you think Mr. Popper's decision about the penguins was right? Why, why not?
- Will Mr. Popper ever come back to Stillwater?
- Do you think the penguins will be safe in the arctic? Why, why not?

THEMATIC/WHOLE LANGUAGE ACTIVITIES

Social Studies
- Study the arctic and antarctic.
- Learn to use the globe and find all the places Mr. Popper wanted to go.
- Students choose a place they want to go and read about it.

Science
- Study penguins.

EXTENDED READING

Ramona the Pest – Beverly Cleary
Grasshopper and the Unwise Owl – Jim Slater
Owls in the Family – Farley Mowat
Fantastic Mr. Fox – Roald Dahl

Name _____

Draw the cover of a book Mr. Popper might read.

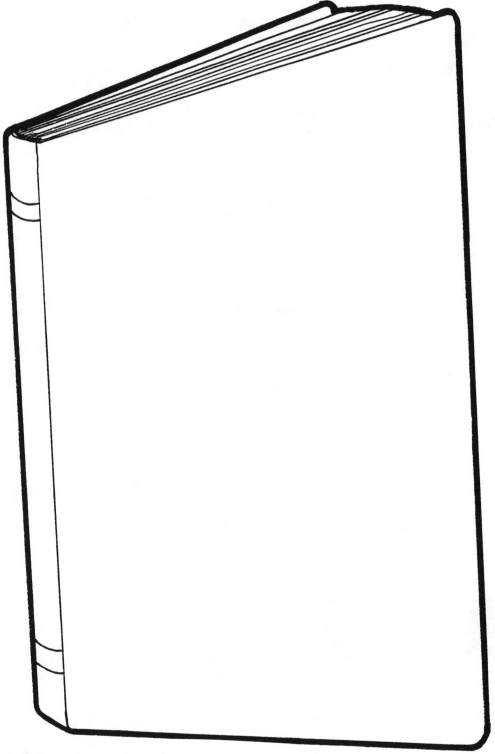

Use after chapter 2 — A Voice in the Air

Name ———————————————————————————————

What would Captain Cook have found in your house to build a nest.

He would find ———————————————————————————

———————————————————————————————————————

———————————————————————————————————————

Use after reading chapter 7 – *Captain Cook Builds a Nest*

Name _____

Write a newspaper story about Mr. Popper's Penguins. Include a picture and headline.

STILLWATER NEWS

_____
(heading)

(picture)

_____

_____

_____

_____

_____

_____

_____

Use after reading chapter 11 – *Greta*

Name _____

Draw the tricks you would teach your penguins to do.

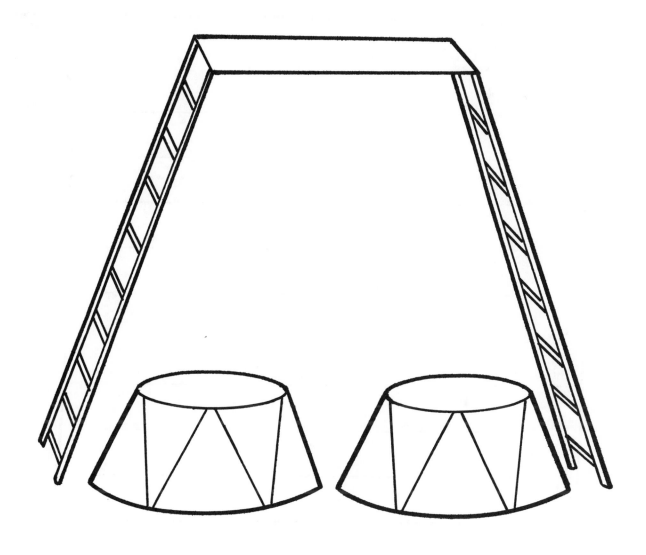

I would teach the penguins to _____

_____

_____

_____.

Use after reading chapter 15 – *Popper's Performing Penguins*

Name _____

Write a letter from Mr. Popper to Mrs. Popper about his trip.

Dear Mrs. Popper,

_____

_____

_____

_____

_____

_____

_____

_____

_____

_____

Love,

Mr. Popper

PADDLE-TO-THE-SEA
Holling Clancy Holling

BEFORE READING ACTIVITY

What kinds of things would you experience if you floated in a stream, through lakes and down to the sea? (Discuss.)

In this story a little carved Indian in a canoe starts out on just such a journey. Listen to its experiences.

AFTER READING ACTIVITY

What do you think happens to Paddle-to-the-Sea after the book is finished? (Chain responses on board.)
Example:

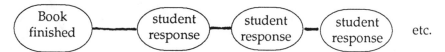

Book finished — student response — student response — student response — etc.

CRITICAL THINKING QUESTIONS

- Would you be able to work hard on something like Paddle-to-the-Sea then let it go? Why, why not?
- If you were any of the people in the book would you be able to put Paddle back in the water or would you keep him? Why?

THEMATIC/WHOLE LANGUAGE ACTIVITIES

Social Studies	• Study the Great Lakes areas. • Study your own lakes and rivers and where they meet the sea.
Art	• Students make their own Paddle-to-the-Sea. • Draw the Great Lakes as described in the book.
Music	• Listen to the "The Wreck of the Edmund Fitzgerald" by Gordon Lightfoot. Learn other seafaring songs.

EXTENDED READING

Other books by Holling Clancy Holling:
Minn of the Mississippi
Seabird

Name _____

Follow the directions and follow the map of the Great Lakes.

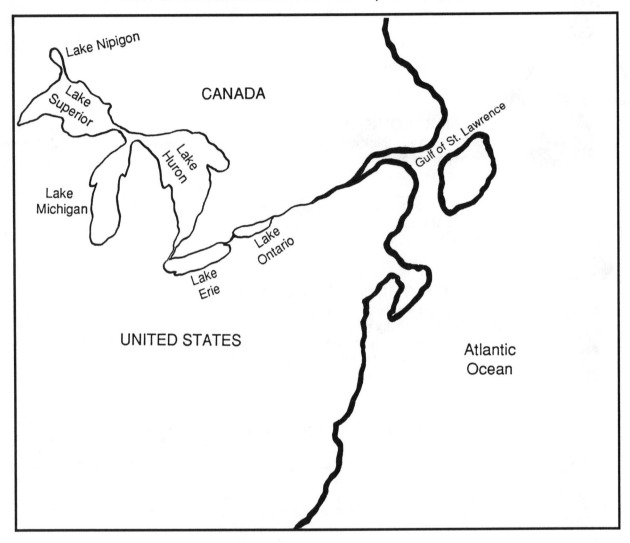

1. Color Canada **yellow**.
2. Color the United States **green**.
3. Color the water **blue**.
    They are: Lake Nipigon
    Lake Superior
    Lake Michigan
    Lake Huron
    Lake Erie
    Lake Ontario
    Gulf of St. Lawrence
4. Color the Atlantic Ocean **blue**.
5. Plot Paddle's trip on this map.

Use after reading chapter 2 – *Long River Reaching to the Sea*

Name —————————————————————————————————

What do you think would have happened if the
French-Canadian man had taken Paddle to his son?

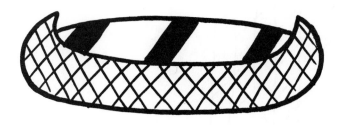

—————————————————————————

—————————————————————————

—————————————————————————

—————————————————————————

—————————————————————————

—————————————————————————

Use after reading chapter 7 – *Paddle Meets a Friend*

Name _____

Draw the fish caught in your fish net. Do not forget to include Paddle-to-the-Sea.

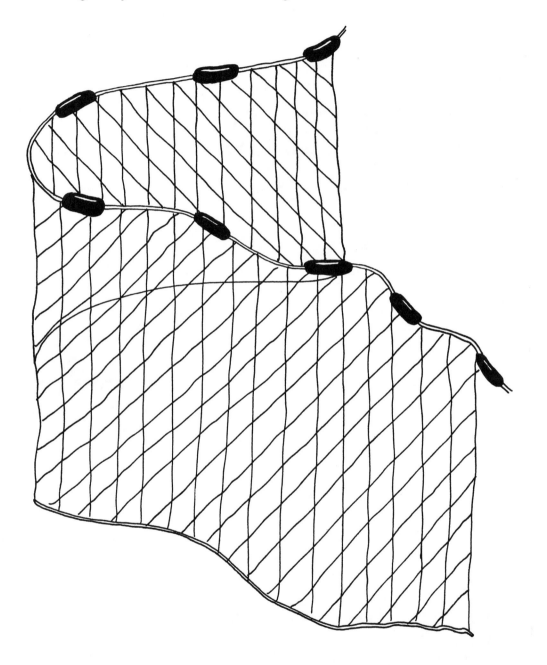

What kinds of fish do you think live in Lake Superior? _____

_____

_____.

Use after chapter 12 – *A Fish Story*

Name _____

Write a newspaper story about Paddle-to-the-Sea.

| Morning Edition | **Buffalo Gazette** | 25¢ |

_____
(heading)

(picture)

_____

_____

_____

_____

_____

_____

Use after reading chapter 22 – *Paddle Takes a Great Fall*

Name _____

What would you have said if you made Paddle-To-The-Sea
and saw it in the French paper?

Use after book is finished.

THE ENORMOUS EGG
Oliver Butterworth

BEFORE READING ACTIVITY
What would you do if you discovered an enormous egg at your house? (Discuss.)

That's what happens to Nate in this book. See what becomes of it.

AFTER READING ACTIVITY
What do you think happens after the end of the book? (Chain responses on board.)
Example:

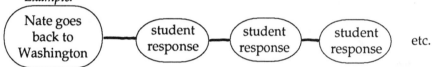

Nate goes back to Washington — student response — student response — student response   etc.

CRITICAL THINKING QUESTIONS
- How do you think Senator Granderson felt after Uncle Beazley got so much support?
- What kinds of things do you think the scientists will learn from Uncle Beazley?
- Do you think that the chicken will lay another egg like that? Why, why not?

THEMATIC/WHOLE LANGUAGE ACTIVITIES

Social Studies   • Learn about how Congress works.

Language Arts   • Students write letters to their congress people about an issue that's important to them.

Science   • Student reptiles that lay eggs.
                     • Learn about dinosaurs.

EXTENDED READING
Other books by Oliver Butterworth
The Trouble with Jenny's Ear
Narrow Passage

Name _____

Draw three things you think might come out of that egg. Describe them.

_____

_____

_____

_____

_____

_____

_____

_____

_____

Name ——————————————————————

Draw a picture and write a telegram from Dr. Ziemer
back to Alfred Kennedy in Washington, D.C.

WESTERN UNION

Alfred Kennedy, Washington, D.C.

——————————————————————

——————————————————————

——————————————————————

——————————————————————

——————————————————————

Dr. Ziemer

Use after reading chapter 6

Name _____

Write a radio report about Uncle Beazley.

Use after reading chapter 9

Name ——————————————————————————

Draw and write how Uncle Beazley is similar and different from an automobile.

SIMILAR

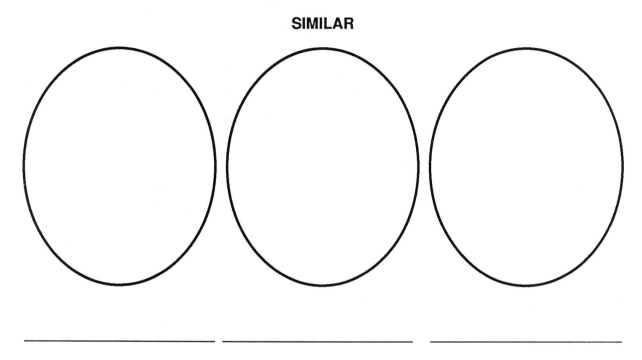

—————————— —————————— ——————————

—————————— —————————— ——————————

DIFFERENT

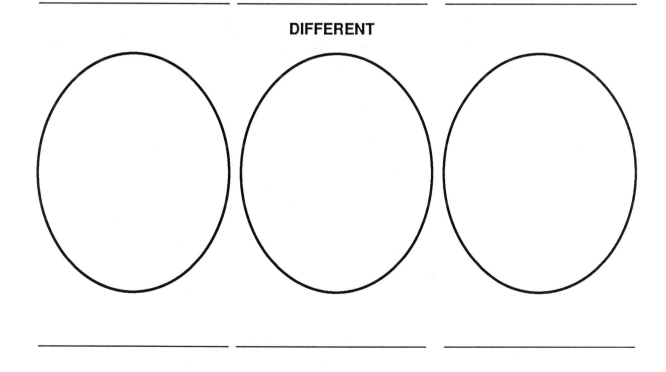

—————————— —————————— ——————————

—————————— —————————— ——————————

Use after reading chapter 13

Name _____

Cut out the folder. Write and illustrate a booklet explaining how to raise a dinosaur.
Use all four sides.

How to

Raise

a

DINOSAUR

Use after reading chapter 17

A LIGHT IN THE ATTIC
Shel Silverstein

BEFORE READING ACTIVITY

What do you think "a light in the attic mean"? Have you ever experienced a light going on in your attic? (Discuss.)

Listen to the poems of Shel Silverstein and see what he thinks "a light in the attic" means.

AFTER READING ACTIVITY

What do you think "A Light In the Attic" means now? Why? (Discuss.)

CRITICAL THINKING QUESTIONS

(Use with individual poems as appropriate.)
• What is real about this poem? What is makes-believe?
• How could the person/thing have solved his/her problem?
• Have you ever felt like this?

THEMATIC/WHOLE LANGUAGE ACTIVITIES

Language Arts   • Write a letter to one of the characters in the book. Tell them why you like them and give them advice.
                  • Students write their own poetry.

Art   • Make a model or diarama of something in the book.

Social Studies   • Students list similarities and differences between themselves and characters/situations in the book.

EXTENDED READING

Other books by Shel Silverstesin:
The Giving Tree	*Where the Sidewalk Ends*
Lafcadio, the Lion Who Shot Back	*Giraffe and a Half*
Who Wants to buy a cheap Rhinoceros?	*The Missing Piece*

A Light In the Attic

Name _____

What would you rather do than dry the dishes? Draw and write your answers.

 I would rather _____

_____

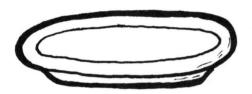 I would rather _____

_____

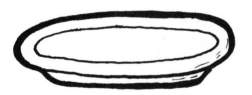 I would rather _____

_____

 I would rather _____

_____

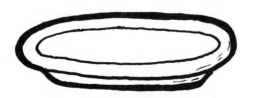 I would rather _____

_____

Use after reading – *How Not to Have to Dry the Dishes*

Name ———————————————————————————————

What is this picture puzzle piece part of?

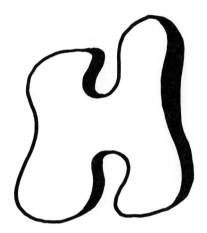

Use after reading – *Picture Puzzle Piece*

Name _____

Where are things in your messy room?

My _____ is on my _____.

My _____ is on my _____.

My _____ is on my _____.

My _____ is on my _____.

My _____ is on my _____.

Use after reading – *Messy Room*

Name _____

Make up a poem about things you have never done.

I have never . . .

_____

_____

I have never . . .

_____

_____

I have never . . .

_____

_____

I have never . . .

_____

_____

I have never . . .

_____

_____

Use after reading – *Never*

Name _____

What will this polar bear find in your refrigerator?

He will find:

_____   _____

_____   _____

_____   _____

Use after reading – *Bear in There*

Name _____

Write a poem about the letter "e" without using it in your spelling.

Use after reading – *Imprtnt*

ART/LANGUAGES ARTS:
Creative Thinking

Name _____

Design your own homework machine. Tell how it works.

My homework machine works by _____

_____

_____.

Use after reading – *Homework Machine*

Name _____

Draw and write how else balloons can pop.

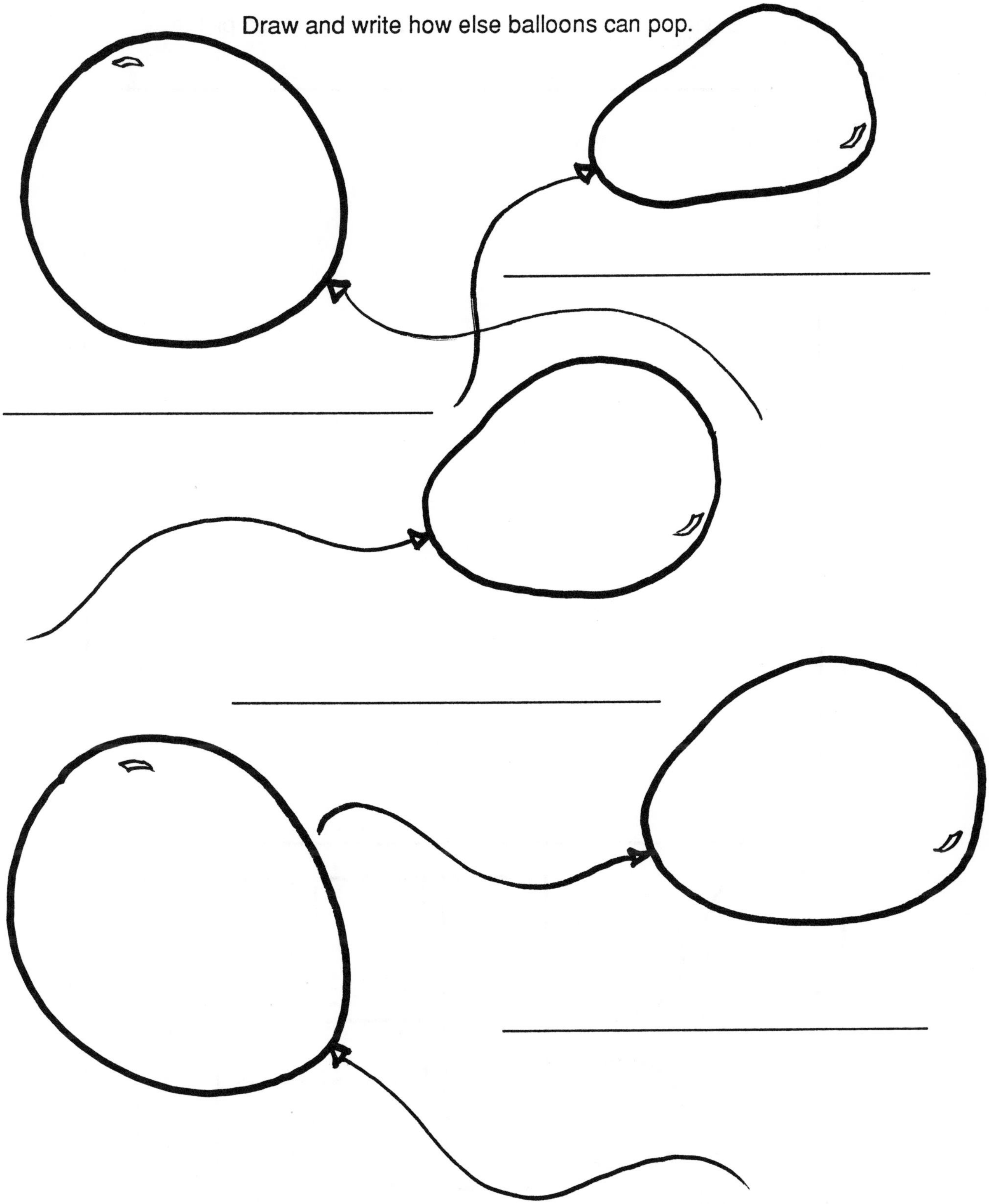

_____

_____

_____

_____

Use after reading – *Eight Balloons*

Name _____

Color and cut out the shapes. Paste them into a picture.

Use after reading – *Shapes*

Name

What would you want to strike for?

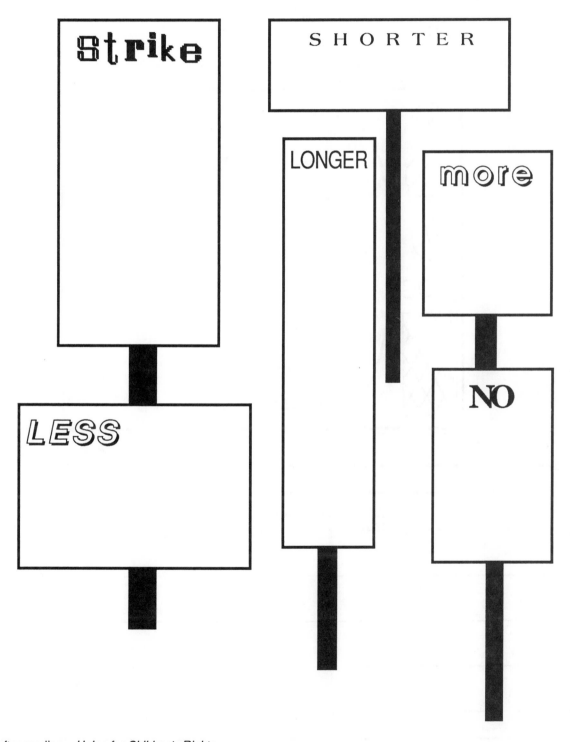

Use after reading – *Union for Children's Rights*

Name _____

Write a T.V. commercial for new and improved, better parents.

_____

_____

_____

_____

_____

Use after reading – *Clarence*

HAILSTONES AND HALIBUT BONES
Mary O'Neill

BEFORE READING ACTIVITY

What colors do you think of with hailstones and halibut bones? What colors does autumn bring to mind?

All the colors of the rainbow are set to rhyme in this poetry book.

AFTER READING ACTIVITY

(Use with individual poems as appropriate.)
What other feelings/images can you think of to go with this color? (List on board.)

Example: Orange
the taste of orange juice
sweet smell of orange blossoms
dusty smell of first rain

CRITICAL THINKING QUESTIONS

(Use with individual poems as appropriate.)
- What is your favorite color? What are your favorite things? See if the poet mentions them in this poem.
- Have you ever felt like a color? How?

THEMATIC/WHOLE LANGUAGE ACTIVITIES

Language Arts	• Write poems and chart stories about colors, feelings and things.
Science	• Take a "color walk" where children draw the things they see and hear in color.
Math	• Graph feelings the children have in response to a specific color.
Example:	Red

	1	2	3	(# of students)				10 etc.
mad								
excited								
emergency								

EXTENDED READING

Surprises – Lee Bennett Hopkins

Name _____

Draw the things that are purple to you.

PURPLE THINGS ARE

_____   _____

_____   _____

_____   _____

Use after reading – *What Is Purple?*

Name _____

Draw what is gold, what is yellow, and what is both for you.

What is Gold?
My gold things are:

_____

_____

_____

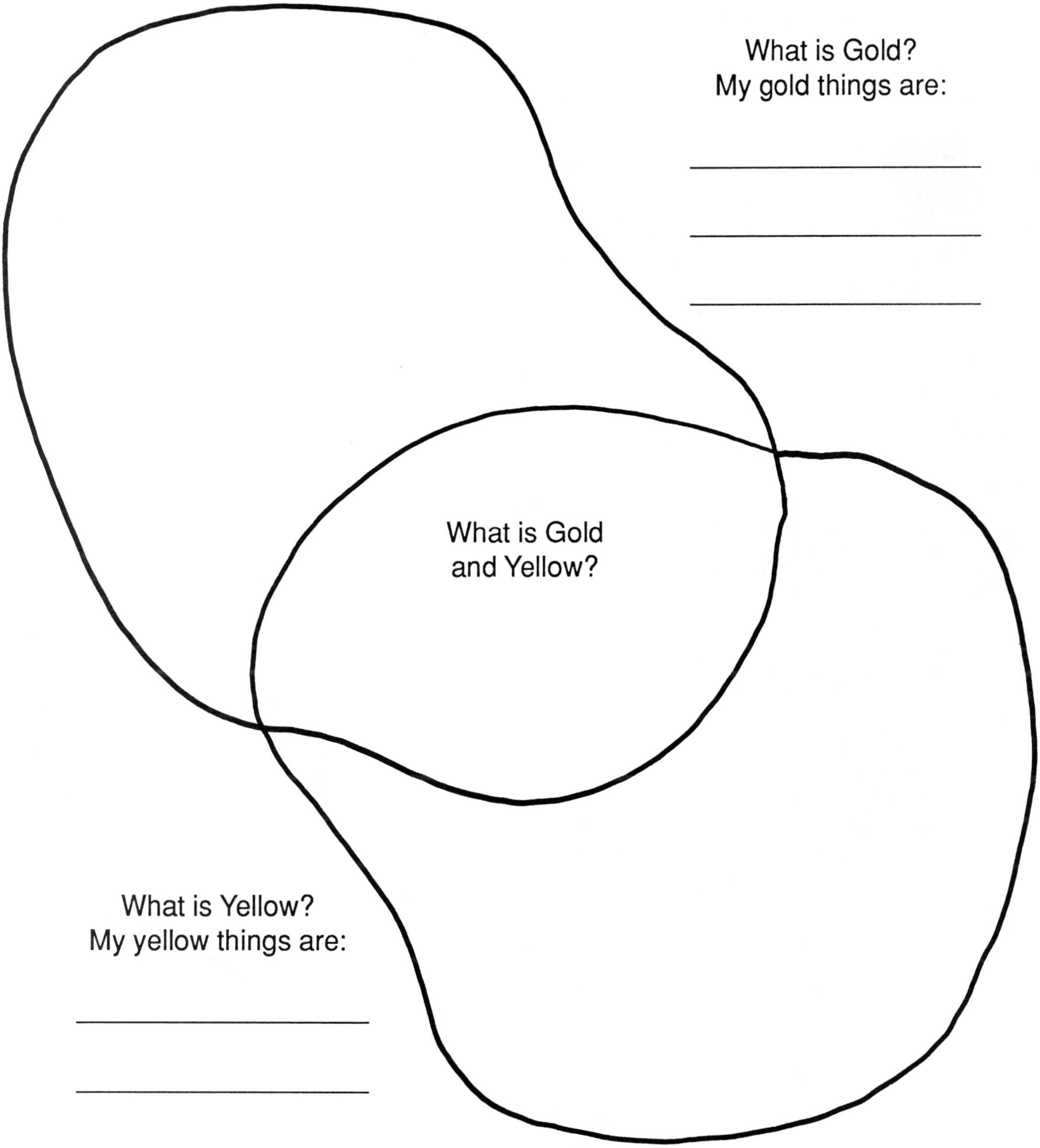

What is Gold
and Yellow?

What is Yellow?
My yellow things are:

_____

_____

_____

Use after reading – *What is Gold* and *What is Yellow*

Name _____

Write a poem about feelings that are black to you. Draw them below.

_____

_____

_____

_____

_____

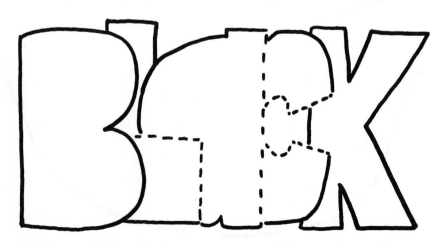

Use after reading – *What Is Black?*

Name _____

Choose another color. How is brown the same and different than that color?

Brown

My color : _____

SAME

DIFFERENT

Use after reading – *What Is Brown?*

Name _____

What are some smells and sounds that are blue to you?

SMELLS

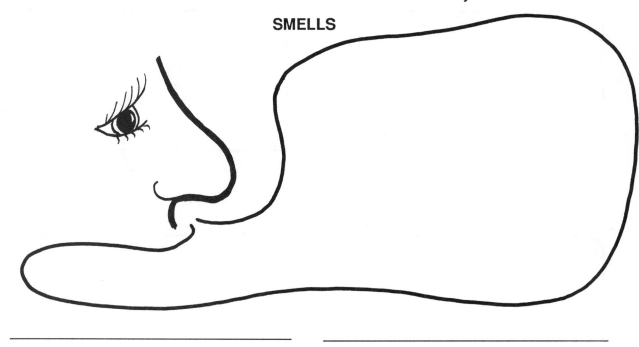

_____   _____

_____   _____

SOUNDS

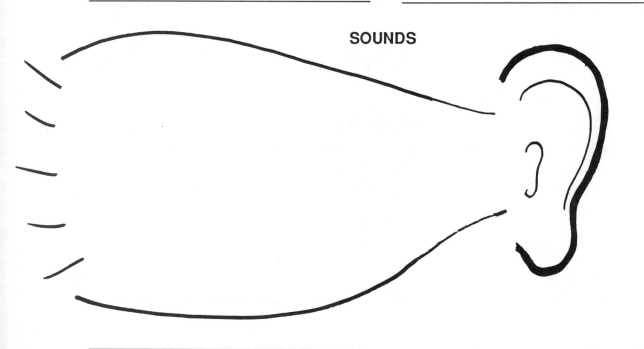

_____   _____

_____   _____

Use after reading – What Is Blue?

Hailstones and Halibut Bones

Name _____

Draw the colors and feelings of autumn.

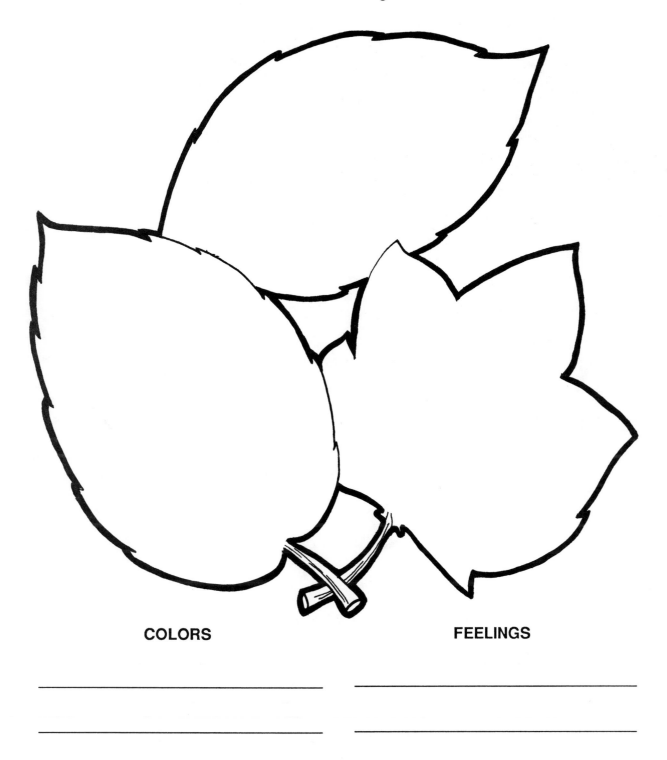

COLORS   **FEELINGS**

_____   _____

_____   _____

_____   _____

Use after reading – *What Is Orange?*

Name _____

Draw and write what red is for you.

Red is:

_____

_____

_____

_____

Use after reading – *What Is Red?*

Name _____

Draw your favorite green things.

Name _____

Color the rainbow with your favorite colors. Write a poem about them.

_____

_____

_____

_____

_____

Use after book is finished.